T...
PACAL VOTAN
Time is the
FOURTH DIMENSION

JOSÉ ARGÜELLES

Layout and setting by Altea Publishing
Printed by Guernsey Press Ltd
Published by Altea Publishing, Parkmount House,
10 St Leonards Road, Forres IV36 0DW, Scotland

"Not at a crisis of nervousness do we stand now, not at a time for the vacillation of flabby souls; but at a great turning point in the history of scientific thought, at a crisis such as occurs but once in a thousand years, such as has not been witnessed for many generations. Standing at this point, with the vista of future achievements before us, we should be happy that it is our lot to live at this time and to participate in the creation of tomorrow."

V.I. Vernadsky, 1932

CONTENTS

Introduction

T(E)=ART,
THE CALL OF PACAL VOTAN

In 1953, when I was a child of 14 years, I discovered the Mayan system of mathematical notation. Unique among all other mathematical systems on the planet which are decimal or based on 10s, the Mayan system is vigesimal, based on 20s. The Mayan system uses a stunningly simple and elegant notational form: a dot for units, a bar for five units, and a 'zero' to indicate positional advances by the power of 20, e.g., 20, 400, 8,000, 160,000, etc. The classic Maya (AD 435-830) of Central America used this mathematical system to great advantage in correlating astronomical time and developing an unparalleled system of calendrics.

As I delved into my lifelong study of Mayan mathematics, I became impressed by the fact that scarcely any researcher (all Western-trained, of course) considered the Mayan mathematic to have any significance as a kind of tool for gauging or critically evaluating our own standards of time, history, mathematics and calendrics. Instead, after an initial curiosity, the Western-trained writers merely accepted the Mayan mathematic as a unique, if baffling, singularity, of no merit or value whatsoever to the modern world.

Not being able to rest with the archeological dismissal of the Mayan mathematic, by the 1970s I began to construct versions of the most unique cornerstone of the Mayan mathematical system: the tzolkin or sacred 260-day calendar, a permutation sequence of 13 numbers (1-13) and 20 icons. In 1983 I made the discovery that a mathematical connection existed between the 260-unit tzolkin and the I Ching/DNA 64-unit code, published in my book *Earth Ascending: An Illustrated Treatise on the Law Governing Whole Systems* (1984). My conclusion at this point was that the 13 X 20 permutation system of the tzolkin was actually the mathematical expression of a higher self-existing galactic matrix through which even DNA, the 'stuff' of life, is coordinated and cycled into comprehensive planetary forms.

The culmination of my first 33 years of research and reflection on the mathematics of the Mayan calendar were published in *The Mayan Factor: Path Beyond Technology* (1987). Here I finalized my hypothesis that the 'classic' Maya, practicing a 'time science' well in advance of anything we know about, deliberately left two clues for modern humanity: the 'long count' of the 13 baktuns or great cycle of history (BC 3113-AD 2012), and the tzolkin or 260-unit sacred calendar. As I demonstrate in *The Mayan Factor*, even the 'long count' is a fractal of the tzolkin.

By 1988 it was clear that I had no choice but to devote my entire life to the final unraveling of the Mayan mathematic code of time so that its significance could impact modern civilization in its entirety. Assisted by my partner and wife, Lloydine, we hit paydirt at the Museum of Time in Geneva, Switzerland in December of 1989. Finally we understood: humanity has evolved historically, unbeknownst to itself, under increasing stress of a false and artificial timing frequency, the 12:60 (12-month calendar, 60-minute hour). As a result, humanity has deviated from nature, and without correcting its timing frequency will end in disaster, sooner than later. The natural, galactic timing frequency was encoded by the Maya in the tzolkin, and is known as the 13:20 (13 galactic tones, 20 solar frequencies).

Following the discovery of the timing frequencies came the rediscovery of the 13-moon, 28-day calendar to replace the erroneous Gregorian calendar, and the codes of fourth-dimensional time Dreamspell, the Journey of Timeship Earth 2013 (1990-91), hitherto unknown to historical humanity caught in its increasingly entropic 12:60 time distortion. *The Call of Pacal Votan* was written in late 1992 (originally with the title *A Treatise on Time*) as a means of making the fourth-dimensional mathematics of time systematic and clear, inclusive of all of the implications for the immediate evolutionary course of humanity.

The 20th century began with the equation $E=MC^2$. The theory of relativity binds space within the speed of light and really says nothing about time. Its applications have produced 50 years of cold war and nuclear terrorism. The Mayan gift of 'time science' has finally been unraveled — and just in time. Before the 20th becomes the last century of human evolution, we offer the corrective equation: T(E)=Art, ((E)nergy factored by (T)ime=Art), where (E) is the energy of any whole system, (T), the 13:20 unifying timing frequency, and 'Art' the result of factoring energy by time. This is why 'nature' is constantly wondrous and artistic. This equation also points to the creative direction humanity could take by rejecting its false timing frequency and returning to natural time.

The process of discovering something as fundamental as the laws governing fourth-dimensional time is one demanding a complete sacrifice of personal, conditioned values in order to arrive at the truth. In its power of transcendence, truth is a calling. The reader will note that this treatise is in 'fulfillment of the Call of Pacal Votan'. This most singular personality of all the 'classic' Maya (AD 603-683) left a sacred center, Palenque, an incomparably spectacular tomb, and a prophecy, Telektonon, Earth Spirit Speaking Tube (1993-95).

I now recognize that my life mission in pursuit of the mathematics of time has been and continues to be at the 'Call of Pacal Votan'. Referred to as 'time's special witness', the personage and presence of Pacal Votan, Galactic Agent 13 66 56, have guided me all along. By the timing of his 52-year cycle of power, AD 631-683, and by the clues he left, Pacal Votan demonstrated his mastery of the Mayan time science. The Maya really did have a mission to leave the 13:20 knowledge of time, precisely for the purpose of offering us the opportunity of correcting our course in time — before it is too late.

As the human responsible for bringing to light the knowledge of time in its true fourth-dimensional form, I recognize the enormity of my task. I ask the reader, as my self, to bear in humility all of the imperatives which this truth commands. In the spirit of the one nameless, all-evolving divine source, I bow in gratitude that I have been instrumented as the vessel of this truth.

Jose Argüelles, Ph.D.
Overtone Moon 11
Kin 216 Yellow Galactic Warrior
Third Year of Prophecy
'Victory Pacifies'
(Gregorian: November 25, 1995)

Overview

THINKING ABOUT THE UNTHINKABLE

Of all the unexamined assumptions and criteria upon which we base and gauge our daily lives as human beings on planet Earth, by far the greatest and most profoundly unquestioned is the instrument and institution known as the Gregorian calendar.

A calendar — any calendar — is commonly understood as a system for dividing time over extended periods. A day is the base unit of a calendar, and the solar year is the base extended period.

The length of the solar year is currently reckoned at 365.24199 days. The Gregorian calendar divides this duration into 12 uneven months — four months of 30 days, seven of 31 days and one of 28 days. On the Gregorian calendar the accrued quarter day is handled by inserting February 29th every four years. This is not necessarily the most logical or the only way of handling the accrued quarter day.

'30 days hath September, April, June and November; all the rest have 31, except for February alone, which has 28 days clear and 29 in each leap year.' So goes the folk rhyme underscoring the illogical nature of the Gregorian calendar. By contrast, a far easier and more logical way to divide the solar year would be by thirteen 28-day months with one extra free day.

The point is this: there is no logical or scientific relation between the exact length of the year and the use of the Gregorian calendar to measure and divide that length.

Nonetheless, the Gregorian calendar is held up as the most perfect instrument for dividing time, and is in use worldwide as the official standard. Although the lunation-based calendars of Islam, the Hindus, Jews and Chinese are still used for religious or ritual purposes, in daily economic and political affairs the Gregorian calendar prevails throughout the planet. How and why did this happen? What is the Gregorian calendar and where did it come from? Why do we continue to use it? Indeed what is the relationship between calendars and human behavior?

If one looks under the heading 'calendar' in the Micropaedia of the 1985 edition of *The Encyclopaedia Britannica*, a full 80% of the entry is devoted to the Gregorian calendar. This exemplifies the unquestioned authority granted to the Gregorian calendar. What is the basis of this authority?

The Gregorian calendar is dogma because no one questions it, nor wants to question it. The Gregorian calendar is the foundation of the 12:60 timing frequency.

All authority granted to this calendar is actually an allegiance to a late medieval Christian timing device. The authority of this device is held by the Vatican, geographically the smallest political state on the planet, yet given full political protection by the major Western powers (the G-7: USA, Canada, United Kingdom, France, Germany, Italy and Japan).

The irregularly numbered and irrationally named 12-month Gregorian Calendar came about as a result of a Papal Bull issued by Pope Gregory in 1572 and implemented October 5-15, 1582. The historical context in which this calendar became the fixed standard is of the greatest significance. European power, instigated by acquisitive material greed and the Church's need to gather all souls under its cross, had literally straddled the globe. Henceforth, no one could receive the 'blessings' of Christianity without receiving the Gregorian calendar.

In Europe itself, the Gregorian calendar succeeded at the precise moment when the final mechanization of time was being achieved. By AD 1600 the 12-month year and the 60-minute hour had become the established standard of time.

Thus, accompanying and giving form to the very origins of modern materialistic science was the final codification of the third-dimensional timing frequency, the 12:60. Needless to say, the authority and impact of this timing frequency was never questioned, much less realized. Though men like Kepler and Galileo were persecuted by the Church, they did not question the authority of the calendar. And so it has been with virtually all men and women of science — they accept without question this calendar by which they live.

It is to the fundamental discredit of all modern science and the society governed by its principles that it has continued to unquestioningly accept living under what is essentially a medieval yoke of time. The Gregorian calendar is a hypnotic spell which holds all the unresolvable issues of history hidden in its illogical sequence of days, weeks, months and years. Following this calendar can only lead to the place where we find ourselves today: a season of apocalypses, where disaster, ignorance and error perpetuate themselves in grinding mindlessness.

The dark apocalyptic disasters of history can only repeat themselves under this medieval yoke of time. This is how Sarajevo could be the flashpoint for World War One in AD 1914, and an unresolved battleground in AD 1995. On an even vaster scale, under this medieval yoke, we see how Babylon at the beginning of history is now the stage-set for the end of history in present-day Iraq.

Clearly, history is not democratic, and democracy itself is a hoax to keep us in the illusion of power and security. History is the script of those in power, and whoever holds the power writes the history. No one was ever asked about the Gregorian calendar, and so we all follow it as if this were the only way to deal with time.

No one has ever considered the effects of the timing frequency or standard under which we live, nor have we ever been given the opportunity to consider 'what if?' Yes, what if we lived under a different standard of time? Ask the Australian aborigine, the Amazon forest dweller, the Native American on the 'res' (reservation) what happened to their time and you will soon see that it is in the interest of the G-7 and the Vatican to keep you confused.

The Gregorian calendar is based on the original Babylonian model which substituted a measurement of space for a measurement of time. Time is not space. Time is of the mind. A circle on a flat plane divided into twelve 30° parts was used as the model for the annual calendar. A circle on a flat plane has 360 degrees (30 x 12). One annual orbit of the Earth around the Sun is $365\frac{1}{4}$ days. The measure of time according to the standard of the circle on a flat plane is irregular, arbitrary and irrational. As is the measure of time, so is the measure of our mind.

In AD 1582, when Pope Gregory XIII cut ten days off the Julian calendar and ordained the final version of the Babylonian calendar, the mechanical clock achieved its final perfection. Using the same flat plane circle of 12, the clock doubled the 12 to 24 hours and the degrees from 30 to 60 minutes per hour.

Taxes, war and government were already secondary institutions of the human mind due to the 5,000-year use of the 12-month calendar throughout the Old World. But combined with the mechanical clock which doubled the measure, the 12:60 artificial timing frequency was locked into place as the irregular and mechanically accelerating mental condition of the human race, setting it apart from the rest of nature. Now added to taxes, war and government was the machine.

Without the mechanical clock there would be no machine, and all industrial technology would be impossible. By adjusting our biological rhythm to the accelerated 12:60 artificial time machine frequency, we humans began the acceleration of our own biological activity, with the consequent time bomb of overpopulation which plagues us today.

The tick-tock of the clock is the artificial heart ('old ticker') of Mammon. Mammon is the diabolical ghost in the machine that is living us, that is using our accelerated biological reproduction to create a total machine world. The triumph of Mammon is the triumph of materialism. The first phase of Mammon was the creation of the Babylonian 12-month government system of taxes and wages for labor. The second phase of Mammon was the clock-based machine.

Today there is no machine without money, no money without a machine, and no nation without money. Nationalism is perverted into the 12:60 dogma of war and money. But in the biosphere all boundaries are illusory.

Time and the Biosphere: Beyond Nationalism

The 12-month Gregorian calendar has nothing to do with the annual biological rhythm of the human species in harmony with the biosphere.

A clock does not measure time. A clock measures increments of space which, projected as increments of time, are valorized into monetary units. Money does not grow on trees. Money is a function of false time.

No one owns the biosphere. No one owns time. True time does

not produce money. Time is of the biosphere.

Thirteen moons, 28 days is the biosphere's measure of the annual human biological rhythm. Twenty-eight days, 13 times a year, is the human female menstruation cycle. Everything is born of woman. To kill a woman, to harm a child, is to destroy the future. This is the 12:60 way, the way of war.

By adopting the 13-moon, 28-day calendar and rejecting the Gregorian calendar, humans will take the first step beyond the collective self-destruction bred by nationalism and the biospheric self-destruction bred by Mammon (money-machine).

More dogma to be questioned: Virtually all governments, the Vatican and banking institutions worldwide operate by the 12-month Gregorian calendar. This calendar denies and covers up the true annual human biological cycle conserved in the body of woman. Why are virtually all government leaders men? Why is it that men make war? Why is it men who run all the banks? Why are only men allowed to be priests in the Catholic Church?

Only by rejecting worldwide the 12-month Gregorian calendar and adopting immediately as the new world standard the 13-moon, 28-day calendar does the human species have any hope of resolving the suicidal deadlock of nationalism and the biosphere-destroying monetary politics which now governs the nations. Only by adopting the 13-moon calendar will endless conflicts such as the Palestinian/Israeli and Bosnian/Serbian ultimately be resolved.

Only by unifying bioregionally under the new calendar which supports all spiritual views and values equally, but does not affirm nationalism, will we find a new covenant to take us beyond war into a peace that is more than just the absence of war.

Insofar as the United Nations affirms and upholds nationalism, it is biospherically obsolete. Insofar as the United Nations affirms world peace, the United Nations' greatest peace-making operation will be to supervise the dismantling of the nation states which it now supports to the detriment of the biosphere, transforming itself thereby into the Autonomous People's Biospheric Union of the One Sovereign Earth.

This the United Nations can do by promoting, adopting and implementing the 13-moon calendar, the 13-Moon Calendar Change Peace Plan and the Pax Cultura Pax Biospherica Five-Year

Plan, effective White Electric Wizard (July 26, AD 1995).

Without the 13-moon calendar change at the top of the list of peace agenda priorities, there will be no lasting peace. If the United Nations can place the 13-moon calendar change at the top of its peace agenda list, it will prove to the people of the planet that it is more than a sub-contractor of the United States State Department.

After 50 years, and more than 150 wars and 20 million war-dead, the 13-moon calendar change is the biosphere's last ultimatum to the United Nations to transcend the dogmas of nationalism and the Gregorian calendar and help bring true peace to planet Earth.

In God We Trust: Concerning the False Religion, Time is Money

The 12-month Gregorian calendar is the annual measure of the dogma 'time is money'. The mechanical clock / 60-minute hour is the daily measure of the dogma 'time is money'. Punching in and out of the time clock is the measure of the worth of our time — in money. This is the essence of 12:60 life. 12:60 is the manifest error in time which we all live, an error which is costing us the biosphere.

Money is the power ascribed to God which is worshipped and feared by all. 'In God We Trust' inscribed on the American dollar bill is the evidence of the dogma that 'time is money' and money is God's most trusted partner.

The American dollar bill is the world standard of the 12:60 dogma 'time is money'. The world's stock markets are the temples where the religion 'time is money' is propagated on a daily basis, five days a week, and its rituals of worship performed. In the stock market all human values translated into shares of competing industries are traded against an index of arbitrarily manipulated monetary units dominated by the presence of the almighty dollar.

'In God we trust, time is money' is the false religion which governs all human activity on the planet today, AD 1995, according to the pseudo-ideology of monetary politics.

In abolishing the 12-month Gregorian calendar and replacing it with the biospherically accurate 13-moon calendar, the foundation of the dogma 'time is money' is destroyed. Destroy the power of money and the power of the machine is also destroyed.

Money is the life-blood of the machine whose heart is the

mechanical clock. The machine is the body of Mammon, the form of Mammon. Mammon feeds on humans. The flesh and bones of Mammon are constructed of the resources of nature. As Mammon proliferates in ever more ingenious forms, human population swells unceasingly, and the biosphere is reduced in its capacity to sustain the entropic, out-of-control excesses of the 12:60 dogma 'time is money'.

As long as the 12:60 timing frequency maintains its inert momentum, the machine can only multiply and propagate, requiring an accelerated increase in humans to devour and natural resources to waste.

Yes, to think about the Gregorian calendar is to think about the unthinkable. But if you do not take the time to start thinking about it now, you may forfeit the only time you have got.

Of Moons, Mayans and the 13-Moon Calendar

Through most of its 26,000-year history, homo sapiens has followed the moon and used moon calendars. The moon is fickle and erratic. It is of nature, subtle and elusive. By current reckoning, it turns on its axis every 29.5 days, the length of a synodic lunation, which is why we always only see one side of the moon.

A synodic lunation of 29.5 days, the duration of one moon cycle seen from the Earth, is only one of the lunation cycles from which lunar compilations can be made. There is also the sidereal lunation cycle of 27.33 days (the time it takes for the moon to return to a fixed point in the sky); the 27.32 tropical cycle (taken from the celestial longitude), and the draconic cycle of 27.2 days (the time it takes the moon to return to the same node).

Right up to the 20th century pre-agricultural humans, such as the Lakota, have followed a vague or unfixed moon calendar. The fact is that during one solar year there is always a 13th lunation which transits from one solar year to the next. The taboo nature of the number 13 seems to stem from the mysterious 13th moon. There is an 11-day discrepancy between the length of the solar year of 365.242199 days and 12 complete synodic lunations of 354.36706 days. The number of days in 13 synodic lunations amounts to 383.5, a discrepancy of 18.25 days more than the solar year.

The discrepancy between days of the solar year and lunation cycles only became a problem for civilized *man*, for woman has always naturally carried the 13 moons within her being. The female menstruation cycle of 28 days is the mean between the synodic lunation cycle of 29.5 days and the other lunation cycles of less than 27.5 days. Factor the mean lunation cycle of 28 days into the solar year and the result is 13 moons, or 364 days, one day less than a mean solar year.

Once agricultural lifestyles were developed in the area of the planet now known as the Middle East, the male priesthood seized power. The question of a calendar became a matter of developing an instrument of power. The male power became associated with the sun, while the female was associated with the moon. A calendar based on the exclusivity of the solar year became paramount. The Egyptian division of the circle into 360°, subdivided into 12 parts of 30° each, provided the male priesthood of Egypt and Mesopotamia with the norm for their celestially oriented 'male solar' hierarchies. This occurred some 5,000 years ago, ca. 3000 BC.

Thus, in Babylonia and Egypt were born the 12 houses of the zodiac (and traditional Western astrology) and the 12-month calendar. Since 12 months of 30 days yield only 360 days, an extra five-day purification period was added on to complete the solar year. The chief function of the Babylonian priests of the calends was to correlate the cycles of the moon with the solar year. By 1500 BC, the system of the 360 degrees of the circle divided into 12 as an approximation of or even as a replacement for the lunation cycles spread to India and China. The 12 is based on the division of space — a circle; not time — the 13 moons.

From Babylonia and Egypt the 'solar power' of the circle of 12 spread to Greece, and thence to Rome. It was Priscius Tarquinus, early emperor of Rome (616-579 BC) who is credited with the development of the calendar from which the Gregorian is ultimately derived. The names of the Gregorian months are all Latin and come from this early Roman calendar.

By the time of the rise of the Christian Church, AD 500-1000, the Roman calendar of 12 months of uneven days in disregard of the lunation cycles was an established fact. At the beginning of the Age of Conquest, AD 1500, it was known as the Julian calendar and was based on the synodic year of 365.25 days. The Gregorian calendar is based on the tropical year of 365.242199 days.

However minute the fractional difference is between the synodic and tropic years, it should not obscure the actuality that the Gregorian calendar is an uneven and illogical distribution of days derived from a male priesthood tradition that stems from Babylonian civilization. It is a tradition of time-reckoning based on the Egyptian division of the circle, which is a division of space and not time, and in which all taboos of the number 13 are fully incorporated.

It is precisely this power of 13, associated with witchcraft and the devil, that the conquering Europeans confronted head-on when they arrived in the 'New World'. For here was a tradition of time and knowledge even more precise and fully developed than in Europe, completely based on the 13. We are referring here to the calendrical and mathematical system of the Maya upon which all Mesoamerican (Mexico and Central America) civilization was based.

There was no chance of real dialogue where the Christian priests and their zealous soldiers were concerned. People of learning were put to death, and libraries burned. The world was deprived of an understanding of time that was based not on the spatial divisions of the circle but on the lunar-galactic power of 13.

Of course, because of the hypnotic spell of the Gregorian calendar — the Dreamspell of history — you will not find a discussion on the Mayan understanding of time in the *Encyclopaedia Britannica* entry on calendars. That is the *Mayan Factor,* the overlooked factor in any accounting of human affairs. Yet if we remain only in the spell of the Gregorian calendar and ignore the Mayan Factor, then truly we are lost.

The Mayan timing frequency is 13:20 and not 12:60. Thirteen refers to the 13 galactic tones or powers of creation, which are also encoded in the 13 moons or annual lunations. Twenty refers to the 20 solar frequencies encoded as the 20 icons or solar seals. Upon this timing frequency was based the *tzolkin* or 260-kin 'sacred calendar'.

Combined with the solar cycle of 365 days, the tzolkin gave the Maya the fractal yardstick by which they could construct calendars and timing systems that demonstrate the harmonic order of the solar system and galaxy in general. Within these constructs, the Maya also maintained their lunar calendars and eclipse cycles of utmost precision.

Because the basis of the Mayan calendar was the 260-kin tzolkin and not the 360° circle, there was no need to correlate the lunation cycle to the solar year through the abstract concept of 'months'. The Mayan mathematic, based on an elegant and more sophisticated dot-bar notation system, is vigesimal not decimal — that is, based on 20s rather than 10s. This gives the Mayan mathematical system a fractal and exponential flexibility not exhibited by the decimal or duodecimal (by 12s) system upon which the Gregorian calendar is based.

Instead of months, the Mayan solar year is divided into eighteen 20-day periods called *vinals*. In actuality the 18 vinals, plus the five-day *vayeb*, were a means of correlating the solar year to the 13:20-based tzolkin.

Long a puzzle to Western archeologists, who early on understood its amazing sophistication and complexity, the Mayan calendar and mathematics have nonetheless been regarded as an anomalous curiosity, with no application to the modern world. Again, this prejudice must be seen as a function of the 12:60 consensus reality.

The fact of the matter is that the Mayan calendar contains the teaching of fourth-dimensional time that has eluded modern science, immersed as it is in the unexamined grip of third-dimensional Gregorian time. The nub of the Mayan teaching is the application of the 13:20 frequency to the creation and implementation of the calendar of the 13 moons.

Part I
CRITIQUE

Description and Nature of the Problem

1. In all of modern thought and civilization there is one dominant, all-inclusive and ever-expanding problem: humankind's alienation from nature. Not being able to resolve this problem, nor being able to think about it in any other way than by the means by which this problem has come about, i.e. through modern science and technology, hope for a positive planetary future grows dimmer every day.

2. Conditioned over many generations by a self-reinforcing languaging which postulates an unquestioned worldview of space and matter, even the thought that the problem of humanity's alienation from nature could be seriously approached by any other method than that of the modern techno-scientific one is treated either with ridicule or as a threat. In this regard the invisible hierarchy of science forms a priesthood whose thriving interest is increasingly bogged down in the protection and promotion of its own system, and hence comes to resemble more and more the antiquated priesthoods of the past whose very existence became a barrier to the truth.

3. The crux of the problem of modern science and the dilemma of a social order totally at odds with the natural order is its exclusive basis in investigations of space and matter and the concurrent and consequent view that time is a function of space; and that while space as a description of matter is of the third dimension, time is of a 'lesser' dimension, the fourth.

Yet even in those areas of experimental research that speak of a space-time continuum, there is no clearly agreed-upon understanding of the nature of time, nor is there a description of time apart from the terms, theories and mathematics of space which is of the third dimension. This applies even to the most discontinuous and non-Euclidean geometries, i.e. Riemann, chaos theory, et. al., which are, nonetheless, all descriptions derived from considerations of space.

4. The confusion regarding time and the fourth dimension results, on the one hand, from the inadequacy of using measurements and instrumentation designed to describe space and matter to measure and define time and the fourth dimension; and, on the other hand, this confusion is the consequence of the self-reinforcing languaging of third-dimensional space science which, becoming bound by its own unexamined mental and limiting cultural standards, is profoundly inhibited in its ability to ask the right questions or to approach the issue of time and the fourth dimension in a genuinely fresh manner. The notion that time and the fourth dimension might possess their own intrinsic qualities, mathematics and epistemology, quite apart from the science and mathematics of space, is totally inadmissible to modern science. In fact, such an admission would mean the end of science as we now know it.

5. A further factor limiting the understanding of modern science is its tendency toward entropic discretion of research, resulting in ever more abstract and abstruse microfields, each with its own language and terminology.

From this factor arise two further consequences. The first is an increasing lack of cross-communication which, with no comprehensive systematic ordering principle whatsoever, creates an overwhelming deluge of information whose usefulness diminishes in proportion to its quantity and lack of total comprehensibility.

The second is the proliferation of technologies and technological 'innovations' which, resulting from a diversity of entropically discrete fields, and without any safeguards as to the ultimate effects of their application, increasingly diminishes the human capacity to withstand the multitude of effects, while impacting the environment in ways that become ever more unpredictable and potentially catastrophic.

In sum, the results of applied third-dimensional space science create problems of both a mental and material nature which, lacking comprehensibility of communication and responsibility for effects, is nothing less than a moral and ethical disaster. This is especially so since, the obvious deleterious effects of modern techno-science notwithstanding, civilization continues to proceed with these methods as if there were no other way.

6. Science — the intelligent capacity to know, define, measure and communicate — is an evolutionary phenomenon whose standards change and vary according to the circumstances and issues facing different phases in the development of intelligence. In spite of the general and inevitable tendency of modern science toward entropic discretion, a counter-trend toward a whole systems approach or methodology has, here and there, made its presence felt. This whole systems approach, rooted more in the biological than the physical sciences, and turning ever more to a consideration of the planet as a single unitary organism or ecosystem, is the only viable context within which a fresh description of time viewed from its own dimension may be undertaken.

7. Such a truly whole systems understanding will have as its end not only an accurate description of the principles of time viewed from its own dimension, but will provide the basis for the establishment of a post-scientific perspective and method by which the problems of human alienation from nature could at last be successfully resolved.

To achieve this grand and noble end implies that a correct understanding of time and the fourth dimension will also offer a new and radically innovative basis for the reordering of human society. In this — the true understanding of time viewed from its own dimension — will at last be launched a logical and comprehensive post-scientific revolution as vigorous as and even further-reaching in its reformulation of human thought and feeling than the scientific revolution of the 17th century. More than just an antidote, the principles of time viewed from its own dimension will provide a positive basis not only for the reorganization of human society, but also for the amelioration of the planetary ecosystem.

A Planetary Whole Systems Approach

The modern techno-scientific system, the science of third-dimensional space, though affecting the entire planetary ecosystem, and possessing widespread acceptance as the normative value system, is by its origins in actuality a mental gloss that is strictly Euroamerican in its cultural roots. A mental gloss is a consensual reality institutionalized as a set of social-mental norms. In its official acceptance as the standard system of knowledge, modern techno-science displaces all other human value systems, i.e. art, Chinese medicine etc. In other words, modern techno-science represents an unyielding and dictatorial monosystemic and monocultural planetary mental gloss, operating at the expense of other cultural value systems.

A monocultural planetary mental gloss is an inherent contradiction in terms which may either end up destroying all that it encounters — including itself — or, through incapacity to evolve any further, evokes in response a comprehensive corrective system. Such a comprehensive corrective system is the planetary whole systems approach, which is of necessity polycultural and polysystemic, and is wholly based on and inclusive of the fourth dimension — time.

In the planetary whole systems approach which I have pursued since 1966, I have worked with three premises:

a) the psychophysical
b) the universal aesthetic, and
c) the Mayan.

All three, though seemingly disparate from each other, are unified by a fourth premise, that of

d) the planetary whole systems.

Individually and together these premises have consistently provided me with a critical perspective on the prevailing monocultural mental gloss, while at the same time offering me deeper research clues concerning the understanding of time from its own dimension. Though my premises and methods may at the outset have appeared original or even bizarre, ultimately they led me to a place of universal understanding whereby I could formulate the basis for an articulation and accurate exposition of time viewed from its own dimension. These premises and their interrelations are summed up as follows:

The Psychophysical Premise

All that we experience and know is actually mental in nature. What we refer to as the physical — that which third-dimensional science measures and exploits — is inseparable from what we think about it. In fact, the world is ultimately only what we feel and know as sensory experience, and sensory experience itself is ultimately determined by and inseparable from mental states and attitudes. The fact that a machine runs is due to its being the activation of a particular set of mental attitudes and projections.

The most thorough experiential exposition of the psychophysical premise is provided by Buddhist meditation techniques, shamatha (mind-calming) and vipassana (mental insight). Needless to say, the mainstream of modern techno-science relegates these techniques and this premise to the subjective borderland of the paranormal. But everything is subjective and relative, including — and in many ways especially — modern science. What is truly subjective and irrational is the unexamined mind.

The problem of alienation from nature results from and is reinforced by the tendency to assume categorically, without understanding, that all thought, theories, concepts and so forth are no more than mental constructs with no intrinsic reality of their own, inseparable from unconsciously held emotional states and unexamined cultural attitudes. It is precisely to address this unfortunate mental condition that hygienic techniques of mindfulness are defined and practiced in order to demonstrate immediately, clearly and directly the psychophysical nature of reality.

The Universal Aesthetic Premise

The impulse to art is a universal attribute of intelligence; intelligence exists as a property of nature and is not solely a human property. Hence, the entire natural order exhibits aesthetic characteristics, and the most enduring human value of all is the tendency toward artistic expression. Artistic expression is intrinsic to human intelligence and builds naturally from the sensory ratios which define and determine our experience of reality. Our reality is the total construct of possible permutations of sensory ratios. Since all sensory experience is intrinsically aesthetic, and all humans possess virtually the same DNA coding and catalogue of sensory ratios, there is a common tendency toward universality of forms and symbols within all human cultures. There is potentially an aesthetic set of forms and experiences for each of the five senses (touch, taste, smell, hearing and sight), while the sixth sense — mind — is (potentially) the synthesizing sensorium. The mind's aesthetic tool is number understood as the harmonic capacity of ratios or proportions to formulate themselves in abstract constructs which nonetheless conform to subliminal or unconscious levels of the varieties of sensory experience. The root of mind is fourth-dimensional, and the fourth dimension is organized by a purely mathematical order known as the radial matrix. To say that the mind's aesthetic tool is number means simply that the whole number system of ratios and proportions which governs the fourth dimension regulates the mind. Whole number proportions and ratios are intrinsically aesthetic. Within the mind, these innate aesthetic ratios and proportions give form to the subliminal and unconscious levels of our sensory experience. In turn, the human expressive urge uses these ratios in the infinite variety of artistic forms and media.

The cumulative impact of different artistic forms and the continuing capacity to regroup and innovate from these forms constitutes the underlying basis of what is known as the history of human culture. The problem of alienation from nature is in actuality the tendency to stratify the capacity for human experience within artificial, already-existing categories which deny the ongoing evolutionary reality of sensory interaction with nature. The liberation of the human mind from the strata of artificial concepts now burdening humanity in rigorously defined feedback loops can only result in a profusion of artistic forms and styles of behavior which defy the comprehension of the present imaginative capacities.

The Mayan Premise

Historically and culturally, the ancient Maya of Mesoamerica represent the attainment of civilization totally apart from the civilizations of Eurasia and Africa, including the Egyptian, Mesopotamian, Indian, Chinese and Greco-Roman-European, which all ultimately impacted and influenced each other to greater or lesser degrees. While the Eurasian civilizations all operated with a decimal (count by 10s) number base and a time ratio based on 12, the Maya operated with a vigesimal (count by 20s) number base and a time ratio based on 13. Expressed through a streamlined, holographic notation system of three symbols (dot for units; bar for five units; zero for base twenty positional) capable of describing infinite orders, the Maya possessed a mathematical complex of calendars and calendrical systems out of all proportion to what might be needed, at least according to the prevailing Euroamerica hypothesis that calendars were developed to assist early agrarian society in determining growing cycles. Positional mathematics is based on the zero. The civilization of the Old World developed a zero and a decimal, base-ten, mathematics which means that the positional system advances by powers of ten, i.e. 10, 100, 1000, 10,000 etc. The civilization of the Maya developed a zero and a vigesimal system, base-20, which means that this positional system advances by powers of 20, i.e. 20, 400, 8000, 160,000, 3,200,000. As can be immediately seen, the base-20 positional mathematic possesses an exponential power of increase, far different from that of the base-ten positional mathematic.

However, since the Euroamerican mental gloss is derived from and systematically rooted in a decimal (10) and duodecimal (12) number and time base, its perceptions are also (unconsciously) skewed according to these mentally formative number ratios. Hence, any evaluation made of the Maya base-20 mathematical and base-13 calendrical systems according to unexamined Euroamerican premises will fall far short of the actuality.

Taken on its own terms, the Mayan calendrical mathematic presents an unparalleled level of harmonic mental sophistication for this planet. This is the essence of what I have referred to as the 'Mayan Factor' (1987) and which, to account for its capacity for harmonic synchronization of planetary and stellar cycles, further presupposes a galactic origin or base for this system. To ignore the nature and implications of this profoundly overlooked factor at this point in time further contributes to the human alienation from nature.

The Planetary Whole Systems Premise

The sum of human experience cannot be separated from its location within the planetary whole system which provides the environment for the development of human intelligence. The stages of the development of human intelligence also refer to a whole system evolution which cannot be separated from the bio-geological whole of which it is a part. The contribution and effects of human intelligence must be precisely placed within the overall structure and development of the whole planet system so that an accurate evaluation may be made. Without such an objective — that is to say, an honest and logical whole systems evaluation — no real progress can be made toward overcoming the essential problem that now perplexes humanity and degrades the planetary environment: human alienation from nature.

In leaving out a genuine understanding of time, and being culturally bound to a specific tradition — the Euroamerican — the third-dimensional science, mathematics and technology of space can no longer logically contribute to an essential understanding of this problem, nor therefore can it lead to any kind of long-term solution. Only viewed from the perspective of a planetary whole systems approach can time begin to be defined on its own terms, thus contributing at last the critical ingredient now sorely lacking in the general mental level of humanity. Such a whole systems definition of time and the fourth dimension will contribute not only to human knowledge but also to the evolution of the species as a whole.

The planetary whole systems approach can be defined according to the contributions of various thinkers and scientists through the course of the 20th century, including: the South African statesman Jan Smuts (*Holism and Human Evolution*, 1926); the resonant field model of French psycho-mathematician Charles Henry (*Generalization of the Theory of Radiation*, 1924); W.I. Vernadsky (*Essays in*

Geochemistry, 1924; *Biosphere*, 1926; *Noosphere*, 1938); Pierre Teilhard de Chardin (*The Phenomenon of Man*, 1955); Buckminster Fuller (*Operating Manual for Spaceship Earth*, 1969, *Synergetics*, 1975-79); Oliver Reiser (*Cosmic Humanism*, 1966); James Lovelock (*Gaia*, 1982); Rupert Sheldrake (*A New Science of Life*, 1982); and José Argüelles (*Earth Ascending*, 1984).

To summarize: Planet Earth is a single unitary evolving organism. The inert or inorganic constitution of the planet, including its core, is ultimately crystalline in origin and nature (rather than incandescent). The evolutionary role of the crystalline core and the general structure of the inner Earth in combination with thermic processes of radioactivity, electromagnetism and geomagnetism are still little understood, but will become more comprehensible the more time is properly understood from within its own dimension. In essence, however, the Earth may be described in terms of a 'resonant field model' of three interactive fields in mutual resonance: the gravitational or geomagnetic; the electromagnetic; and the biopsychic (Henry, 1924). These three fields are dynamically interposed in the biosphere.

On the surface of the planet, which can be chemically divided into inert and living bodies, is the biosphere, a thin unitary envelope in which the most complex levels of change and evolution take place. The recent tendency has been to refer to this meteorologically volatile zone, the biosphere, as the ecosphere. Forming the outer limits of the biosphere is the ionosphere, some 60-70 miles above the Earth's surface. The inner electromagnetic conductor of the ionosphere is complemented by the outer electromagnetic conductor, the Van Allen Radiation Belts, some 9,000 to 11,000 miles distant from the Earth's surface. From thence spreads the magnetosphere, extending out in a tail-like form as much as 40,000 miles. The purpose of these electromagnetic belts is to filter solar-galactic radiations according to the dynamic needs of the evolving biosphere.

Humanity, as a whole organism, is a subcorpus of the larger corpus of life, defined by Vernadsky as 'the unity of the whole living matter in the biosphere'. The active attribute of the biosphere is due to the capacity of living matter to incessantly liberate energy capable of doing work. The history of the biosphere is a process of stages of colonization of living matter. Teilhard de Chardin refers to the human process of colonization of the biosphere as the hominization of the planet. To be understood properly, human intelligence and its cultural/technological expansion must be seen as a function of the most recent geological era, the holocene (12,000 BPE), while the overall environmental impact of humanity must be regarded as an actual geological shaping force.

The interactive feedback of the living subcorpus *homo sapiens* transforms the biosphere through an intermediate historical phase, the technosphere, into the noosphere, the planetary mental envelope. The transformation of the biosphere into the noosphere is not yet complete but is considered to be a necessary and inevitable conclusion to the interactive bio-geocultural feedback loop commonly referred to as the spread of human technological civilization. According to Teilhard de Chardin, once the radiation of humanity over the planet (planetary hominization) reaches the point of a complex technological network of (electronic) communications — the planetary nervous system — then the final phase of human evolution sets in: the planetization of humankind.

Vernadsky speaks most precisely of this process in terms of

"... that immense new form of biogeochemical energy which is represented in the biosphere by the technological work of man, complexly guided by his thought. It is interesting that the increase, in the course of time, of machinery in the structure of human society also proceeds in geometrical progression, just like the reproduction of any kind of living matter, man included ... Statesmen should be aware of the present elemental process of transition of the biosphere into the noosphere.

"The fundamental property of biogeochemical energy is clearly revealed in the growth of free energy in the biosphere with the progress of geological time, especially in relation to its transition into the noosphere." (1938)

Discovery of the 12:60—13:20 Timing Frequencies

Following the pioneering work of Vernadsky, who died in 1944, and Teilhard de Chardin, all of whose work was published after his death in 1951, came the discoveries of the Radiation Belts and DNA in 1953. From these additions to knowledge of the whole planet system, the physicist Oliver Reiser expanded on the concept of the noosphere, describing it as the 'planetary Psi Field' (1966). In Reiser's conception, the Psi field is more than just a mental envelope; it is a mental field which is interactive with the Earth's electromagnetic field and with the DNA, which is the code governing the unitary corpus of living planetary matter. In 1969, Buckminster Fuller expanded on the systems model of the planet in his description of Spaceship Earth (1969), and James Lovelock (1982) gave the whole systems approach an animistic twist with his Gaia hypothesis: that the different interdependent biogeochemical processes of the Earth are tantamount to the creation of a living organism, Earth or Gaia.

Fuller's main contribution to the development of the planetary whole systems approach, however, is in his emphasis on the primal synergy of the tetrahedron. As the simplest geometrical structure, the tetrahedron is one of the few links that connect the geometry of third-dimensional space with the fractal ratios of fourth-dimensional time.

In the development of the concept of the noosphere or psi field, Vernadsky and Teilhard de Chardin both speak of a transition point at which the biosphere transforms into the noosphere or psi field. Understanding the 'when' of this critical transition points to the fundamental problem of time, which Vernadsky himself, acutely aware of the limitations of the geometries and mathematics of space vis-à-vis time and the fourth dimension, addressed again and again in his later work.

Summarizing the work of Teilhard de Chardin and Reiser (I was not yet aware of Vernadsky's contribution) in *Earth Ascending* (1984), I extended the notion of the noosphere or psi field into that of the 'Psi Bank'. As a function of the planetary mental envelope, the Psi Bank is described in terms of its memory-generating and storage capacity. As such it is intimately connected to a planetary timing frequency or evolutionary timing factor. Connected with the construct of a whole planet system memory bank is Rupert Sheldrake's hypothesis of the morphogenetic fields as a formally causative factor in the evolution, self-regulation and mutation of the living corpus of the biosphere.

Prior to the transition of the biosphere into the noosphere, the psi bank is unconscious. Following this transition it becomes conscious, corresponding to Teilhard de Chardin's planetization of humankind. Accordingly, I hypothesized along with Teilhard de Chardin and W.I. Vernadsky that this transition point, which is also an evolutionary moment, was imminent. Incorporated into a description of the expanded storage and memory-generating qualities of the psi bank and accounting for its timing capacities are mathematical formulae which I discovered relating the 64-unit genetic code (also formulated as the I Ching or Book of Changes) with the Tzolkin or 260-unit Mayan 'calendar code'. In this way the Euroamerican consensual gloss was breached, resulting in an even more universal description of the planet's mental field.

The question of the biospheric-noospheric transition point and planetary timing frequencies was addressed again in *The Mayan Factor* (1987), which pinpointed a shift within the planetary noosphere-psi bank occurring precisely on August 16-17, 1987. Popularly known as the Harmonic Convergence, this globally observed event was proof that my hypothesis possessed a degree of accuracy. The hypothesis was this: the Mayan calendric system describes a galactically activated timing frequency whose norms are defined by the unique 20:13-base Mayan mathematical system.

Even if the Harmonic Convergence was merely the popular imagination catching on, why did it catch on to such an abstract idea precisely at this exact moment? My hypothesis was that the Harmonic Convergence was successful because this moment was an awakening within the collective unconscious of a prophetic truth encoded in the 'Long Count' system of the Mayan mathematics. Hence I was driven to understand the full nature of this unique mathematical system and its power of possessing prophetic truths within its mathematical structures.

This hypothesis further posits that as of these dates in 1987 the planetary biosphere would enter a 26-year transition zone whose effects would be evident in widespread social and environmental changes.

A further aspect of this hypothesis is that the timing frequency currently regulating the psi bank would shift, and that what was previously unconscious would become conscious, i.e. the manifestation of the psi bank itself. According to this hypothesis, this shift implies the ending of an entire cycle of human history. Coming to an end would be the collective mental field dominated by third-dimensional space science with all of its entropic encumbrances and social manifestations while, concurrently, there would be an entry into a phase governed by a genuinely fourth-dimensional science of time. With this evolutionary achievement would come the possibility of ending the current alienation from nature, replaced instead by a return to a mental field characterized as a synthesis of human and natural orders, the planetization of humankind and the realization of the planetary whole.

Following the testing point of my hypothesis, the Harmonic Convergence, I turned my attention to a definitive understanding of the mathematical codes underlying the Mayan calendar. In 1989 my partner Lloydine and I made the discovery of the 12:60—13:20 timing frequencies. This discovery is a genuinely new contribution to human understanding. From it we were able to transcribe the Mayan codes into an actual working form and set of mathematical proofs and demonstrations entitled *Dreamspell, The Journey of Timeship Earth 2013* (1991).

The essence of the discovery of the timing frequency is a simple one. The 12:60 refers to an unconsciously accepted order of time that is artificial in nature. Twelve refers to the codification of daily time into an irregular and arbitrary calendar of 12 months. Originated in Babylonia, the final historical form of the 12-month system was instituted in 1583 by the Vatican as the Gregorian calendar, which is now accepted as the standard in use world-wide. Sixty refers to the equally arbitrary division of the day into 24 (2 x 12) hours of 60 minutes each. The result of the 12:60 is the creation of a timing frequency whose mental field of consciousness is dominated by mechanization and a third-dimensional science of space-matter. Unconscious acceptance of this 12:60 timing frequency is the single most contributing factor to the problem of human alienation from nature.

The timing frequency discovery further demonstrates that the division of the solar year into 12 periods or months is an arbitrary one based on divisions of the circle, a construct of the geometry of space, into 12 parts of 30 degrees or days each. From the outset, the stream of civilization originating in Mesopotamia was rooted in space, and what it thought to be time was only a measure of space.

The antecedents of the Gregorian calendar find their origin in Egypt and Babylonia, ca 3000 BC, at which time the spatial geometry of the circle arose. The timing of this occurrence in the ancient Mideast corresponds closely to the Mayan timing frequency which describes a 5126-year 'great cycle' beginning in 3113 BC and ending in AD 2013.

Only by contrast, from our investigation of the mathematical codes of the Mayan calendar, were we able to discover the 13:20 timing frequency. This frequency is not based on a geometry of space, but on a true understanding of time as the fourth dimension. Here at last was the demonstration of a mathematics of the fourth dimension based on the 13 rather than the 12 and operating on the more sophisticated vigesimal rather than decimal mathematics.

In the 13:20 frequency, which is a natural galactic timing frequency, 13 refers to a recapitulative '13 tone cosmology' embodied in a form which we came to know as the wavespell. It is important to keep in mind that the fourth-dimensional terminology is new but it is not difficult to comprehend. In fact, the mathematical order of the fourth dimension is far simpler and yet more comprehensive than that of the third dimension. The 20 refers to a frequency code embodied in the 4 x 5 permutational order or the notational system itself, otherwise known as the 0-19 code. The 20 units of this code are also translated into a color-coded iconic language consisting of 20 symbols or solar seals.

Inherent in the 13-tone wavespell is a calendar of 13 perfect moons or months of 28 days each. 13 x 28 yields 364 days, the 365th day being 'outside of time', and designated green day, a day out of time. This scientific and mathematically perfect calendar is intended to be the replacement for the irregular 12-month Gregorian calendar. Because both the Gregorian and 13-moon calendars operate with 52 seven-day weeks annually (364 days), the 13-moon wavespell calendar provides a perfect daily transition tool for humanity to pass from the third-dimensional timing frequency, which now dominates it, to the fourth-dimensional timing frequency of 13:20.

I cannot sufficiently emphasize how critical it is for humanity immediately to replace the irregular 12-month calendar with the perfect calendar of 13 moons. The physical act of replacing one calendar with the other has the potential for uniting human consciousness in a moment of singular determination which in itself will cause the next shift point assisting the biosphere in its transition into the noosphere, and the approaching conscious manifestation of the psi bank. This act would place humanity in the new timing frequency of 13:20, and it would be an act whose consequences are almost inconceivable from our present vantage point.

Such, in brief, is the background regarding the establishment of the mathematical principles of time and the fourth dimension, principles which are totally apart from third-dimensional space-matter science, and which represent the solution to the crisis in human civilization and scientific thought.

Part II
PRINCIPLES

The Fourth Dimension: Qualities and Nature of Time

1. Just as air is the atmosphere of the body, so time is the atmosphere of the mind. If the time in which we live consists of uneven months and days regulated by mechanized minutes and hours, that is what becomes of our mind: a mechanized irregularity. Since everything follows from mind, it is no wonder that the atmosphere in which we live daily becomes more polluted, and the greatest complaint is: "I just don't have enough time!" Whoever owns your time, owns your mind. Own your own time and you will know your own mind.

2. There are two essential characteristics of time, which is the fourth dimension: mental and aesthetic. Time is mental because it is experienced and known through the mind. Mental cultivation is basic to the experience of time. Time is aesthetic because it consists of different whole levels of order whose proportions and ratios are consistent across scale, each level or order of which is reflected holographically in every other. Aesthetic contemplation and artistic activity are the object and expressive reflex of time. As mind is the root of time, the sensory ratios of artistic experience are the expression of time.

   Because of its unconscious immersion in the third-dimensional level of space, which is commonly known as the material plane, the subcorpus humanity as a species or collective whole has not yet understood or risen to the level of conscious fourth-dimension operation. Unconscious participation in the fourth dimension is common through dreams and related states as well as the varieties of often barely tolerated artistic expression. The experience of time as the fourth dimension does not deny but enhances and gives ordered context to the sensual experience of the third dimension.

3. The fourth dimension is frequently associated with the after-death

state. It may be asked: Is it not a contradiction to speak of the living experience of time as the fourth dimension, and yet speak of the fourth dimension in reference to the after-death state? There is no contradiction. Much as space penetrates all solids, time as the fourth dimension permeates the living as well as the pre-birth and post-mortem states of being which extend beyond the living corpus.

Within the realm of the physical plane or third dimension, the permeation of time is known and experienced as 'the now'. There is only one now, and at the same time there are an infinite number of nows for an infinite number of beings. This now moment, which is without measure and intangible, experienced through mind but capable of accelerating nervous excitation and awareness through all of the senses, is no different than the gateway experience opening into the post-mortem state. It is true that there is a realm of fourth-dimensional experience existing apart from the daily experience of the third-dimensional body. Yet this realm can be accessed through the cultivation of the mind in the now. The fundamental technique for cultivating this state of nowness is referred to as 'Practicing the Universal Equality of Awareness' (see Appendix).

4. From the point of view of the fourth dimension, the distinctions made between the living and the non-living are functions of the dualism of mind fostered by exclusive reliance on methods of third-dimensional science, which further reinforce already-existing erroneous thought patterns fixed in unexamined beliefs regarding 'life' and 'death'. Once the art and science of fourth-dimensional time are properly understood and practiced, common current third-dimensional beliefs, distinctions and practices regarding life and death will alter greatly.

5. Space is materially or sensually tangible, time is mentally tangible. Space is the third dimension. Time is the fourth dimension. In relation to space, time is intangible and immeasurable. In relation to time, space is an infinitely locatable point. Though time may be intangible and immeasurable by the third-dimensional standards of space which are finite and self-limiting, within the standards of the fourth dimension, time has its structures which, being infinite,

are defined by ratios and proportions rather than by limiting equations and geometries of forms. These ratios and proportions of fourth-dimensional time will be dealt with in their entirety following the chronomantic description of the three universal whole orders.

6. The three universal wholes given order by fourth-dimensional time are the galactic, the stellar and the planetary. Each of these orders is a holographic projection of the others. Time as the fourth dimension moves from the largest-scale whole to the smallest. The largest-scale whole is the galaxy or galactic order. What we experience astrophysically through our eyes and third-dimensional instrumentation is merely the physical aspect or outer garment of the galactic whole. As a multitude of subsets of different star systems which nonetheless retain a resonant relation to each other and to the whole, the galactic order itself is maintained by the fourth-dimensional ordering principle of time. The typical spiral form of the galaxy is an aesthetic third-dimensional reflection of the fourth-dimensional ordering system of time which is infinitely aesthetic and mental in origin and nature.

The descriptions of ultimate origins and endings (big bangs and black holes) are merely projections of the third-dimensional mind immersed in its dualistic belief in maintaining a distinction between life and death. Time as the fourth dimension is without beginning or end. There are only cycles within cycles within cycles. Cycles merely define levels and stages of impermanence, which is the chief characteristic of all physical-plane third-dimensional phenomena. The planetary cycle is contained within the stellar cycle; the stellar cycle is contained within the galactic cycle; the galactic cycle is contained within the universal whole; the universal whole is a self-created, self-sustaining mental creation beyond our present capacity to fathom.

7. Planet Earth is not a spaceship, but a timeship. A spaceship, defined as an object following a trajectory in space, nonetheless experiences and is limited by time. No matter how 'far' the spaceship is thought to travel, it cannot escape the variables of time which condition its impermanence. Even 'immobility' experiences time.

All any third-dimensional object can do is maintain its own space. Even a spaceship sailing through space must maintain its own objectified space. A spaceship travels in space. Its capacities are finite; its goals self-limited. A timeship travels in time. Its capacities are infinite; its goals immeasurable.

A spaceship supporting life is further limited by its finite space to a threshold of propagation and multiplication of species beyond which there can only be three choices: stasis, self-destruction, biomutation. (See Postlude: Vernadsky's Biomass Constant: an Equation in Time.)

A planet is a single object moving in its own space. Rotating on its own power a planet maintains its own space as a spiralling orbit around a stellar body. Through resonance with its stellar order, a planet becomes a timeship. A timeship maintains its space in order to afford a conscious experience of the infinite ratios and cycles of time. If the chief characteristics or qualities of time are the mental and the aesthetic, a planetary timeship is one possessing an intelligence capable of crafting itself into a mentally conceived and projected whole aesthetic order or system. This is possible because time is a superior mental order that encompasses and moves through the three universal levels or wholes — the galactic, the stellar and the planetary.

Through conscious self-reflection, the smallest planetary whole can holographically experience and know the other two levels, the stellar and the galactic. A planetary timeship presupposes a type of biosphere capable of transforming itself into a noosphere, and a noosphere capable of manifesting a psi bank. The existence of a psi bank itself presupposes an intelligent intentionality existing at a level beyond and preceding the evolution of the noosphere and psi bank, and capable of instrumenting a universal memory field to be released in different stages through the galactic timing frequency, 13:20.

8. The fourth-dimensional body of a planetary timeship is known as the holon. The holon is the term given to the whole order or structure of fourth-dimensional time, be it at the galactic, stellar or planetary levels. Each holon at each level possesses the same fractal ratios and properties, and hence a common field of resonance can

be established from the planetary to the galactic levels. The structure of the planetary holon, which may be thought of as the fourth-dimensional skeleton of the planet, is an icosahedral or 20-sided pattern. Each of these 20 sides or facets is in actuality a tetrahedral form. Reduced to its essentials, any holon has as its underlying structure the tetrahedron, the primary and quintessential geometric form.

As the galactic level is the sum of a subset of star systems, and the stellar level is the sum of a subset of planetary systems, so the planetary system is the biogenic sum of a subset of interacting species and inert orders. In all three whole levels, the interacting subsets create and are determined by fields of resonance. A field of resonance may be understood either unconsciously or consciously. Ultimately the making conscious of a planetary field of resonance is a matter of free will. That is, the question of transforming a biosphere into a noosphere is a matter of choice of the intelligence of the dominant planetary species. To make this choice is to activate the holon or planetary timeship, to transform the biosphere into the noosphere, and to bring into conscious manifestation the psi bank.

9. The chronosphere is the fourth-dimensional field created by a planet holon in resonance with the rotation of the third-dimensional planet body. The basic fourth-dimensional unit of the chronosphere is the kin, the planetary standard of time which corresponds to the duration of a single rotation of the axis, one day-and-night. A single day-and-night rotation, or kin, is the registration of one biospheric pulsation of a single whole organism, planet. Since a kin is a fourth-dimensional unit, its holographic properties are infinite. In this way, though a kin is the registration of but a single biospheric pulsation, due to its holographically resonant properties the information contained within a kin may be infinitely expansive and holographically all-inclusive.

Through the pulsation of sequences of kin, defined by the 260 units of the fourth-dimensional galactic spin (see below), the planetary chronosphere is the encapsulating form which contains the information-bearing properties of the psi bank. As the fourth-dimensional form in time of the planetary holon, the chronosphere

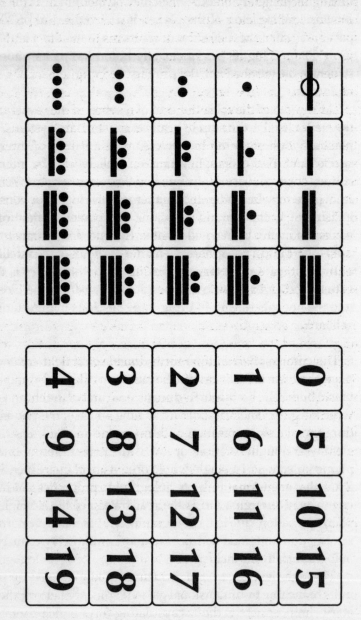

0-19 GALACTIC NOTATION

extends from the planetary core outward 40,000 miles, encompassing the magnetic sheath. The chronosphere is the information constant holding the psi bank in place within the noosphere. The form and pattern of the psi bank conforms to the daily and cyclic galactic patterning of the chronosphere.

Through duration in its space, the chronosphere builds up its information or free energy in geometrical progression, corresponding both to the evolution and expansion of the planetary living matter, and to the ecologically impactful and biogeological transformation of the human species within the planetary whole system. Such a build-up of unutilized and hence unconscious information/energy can be catalyzed at the biospheric-noospheric transition point to assist in the rapid mutation of the species and, indeed, of the entire ecosphere so that the psi bank may manifest and the next evolutionary level be easily attained. Once the planetary noosphere and the psi bank are activated, the chronosphere becomes self-regulating, so that the planet itself may evolve into a consciously realized aesthetic whole.

10. The free energy accumulated by the chronosphere is referred to as g-force or the fifth force. A planet consciously in time renews itself on g-force. It is the infinitely renewable galactic energy source. The g-force is the medium of the galactic synchronization beams, which themselves appear in accord with galactic timing codes. Available g-force increases with the increase of synchronization of the single planetary biospheric organism, kin after kin. The g-force is the transmutative energy which facilitates interdimensional interaction and reciprocity. Fourth-dimensional energy is fourth-dimensional information. The study and comprehension of the varieties of these transmutative interactions is referred to as chronobiology.

11. Chronobiology as it is presently understood refers to the study of the effects of time on living systems, especially rhythms and cycles. From the perspective of time in its own dimension, chronobiology refers to the interdimensional extension of conscious living third-dimensional forms into their fourth-dimensional correspondences. Chronogeology, likewise, refers to the study of the

planet extended into the rhythms and patterns of the fourth dimension. Just as a third-dimensional planet has its fourth-dimensional holon and chronosphere, so the third-dimensional human unit has its fourth-dimensional holon and chronosphere. The realization of the planet whole systems evolutionary future requires that the fulfillment of the human species come about through the equal fulfillment of each third-dimensional unit in conscious relation with its fourth-dimensional holon. As the individual becomes more collective, the collective becomes more individual. The communion of individual holons is attained in the total identification of the individual holon units with the planet holon. This condition is referred to as 'Universal Transcension' (see Appendix 2).

At present the human race is almost universally unconscious of the exact relation of its body to its holon, and chronobiology is at best at a primitive stage of development. However, in the present knowledge of DNA coding combined with environmental aesthetics and release from the 12:60 timing frequency, the field of chronobiology may rapidly advance. In essence, while the DNA code recognizes 64 codons and 20 utilizable amino acids, the chronobiological code encompasses these third-dimensional biological building blocks within a 260-unit galactic enzyme code referred to as 'galactic signatures' (see below). Within the chronosphere, the 260 galactic enzymes or signatures are 'fed' by the g-force and this is the energy available to humans who assume their galactic signatures and become planetary kin. Since the psi bank contains the registrations of the 260 enzymes, the human unit as planetary kin has the opportunity for creative interaction with the psi bank and can become a factor in bringing about its conscious activation.

12. Chronomancy is the science and art of fourth-dimensional time considered as a whole system where science is knowledge and art is practice. Chronomancy has specific application as an intrinsically divinatory and oracular comprehension of events set within the holographic framework of the interdimensional information system which connects the three levels: galactic, stellar, planetary.

Oracular is used here in the sense of an authoritative communication whose information is immediately applicable. Divinatory refers to the process of direct intuitive perception by which the oracular communication is obtained. Because of the discovery of the mathematical proofs of the fourth dimension as well as their demonstration through an empirical form made universally available as the Dreamspell codes of galactic time, the divinatory oracular method of chronomancy is not one that can be usurped by a priesthood or an elite, as has been the case with all historical knowledge systems inclusive of 12:60 science. Rather, it is for each human as an autonomous unit in relation to its holon to chronomantically divine and to know for itself. The realization of this condition of human autonomy, which has the profoundest social, political and cultural ramifications, represents the next evolutionary advancement, and indeed fulfillment of the species *homo sapiens*.

From the 12:60 perspective, time as a mental construct is a system of sequential terms for determining the relationships which any event has to an arbitrarily conceived 'past' or 'future'. In this conception time is a linear model, the self-reinforcing product of a strictly deterministic mental attitude, profoundly conditioned by a dualistic belief in the absoluteness of life and death. Chronology is then little more than a process of dating events within an arbitrarily conceived scale of sequential relationships. In this mental construct, what is gone is dead, and what is to come is unknown. Prediction is given validity to the degree that it bases itself on known data derived from the narrow confines of this sequential linear mental construct. For this reason 12:60 prediction is little more than the tendency to project accelerated versions of itself by terms of geometrical progression into a future increasingly crowded by further technological 'solutions'.

By contrast, chronomancy operates from a superior fourth-dimensional mental construct in which time is known and experienced as a radial matrix: a self-existing system of ratios which govern the rhythms of living matter as well as of all celestial bodies, stars, galaxies and planets, in relation to themselves and to each other. As is demonstrated by the planet body Earth in its rotation on its own axis and its orbit around its local star, time is in the nature of a cyclical vortex. Within this cyclical vortex there are repeatable sequences or rounds of days or kin. To describe the rounds of days or kin as linear goes totally against the intrinsic spin and rotational power of the planet. Within this cyclical vortex (a galactic spin) there is a set of informational time event constants causing each day to differ from every other day, and yet endowing each day with qualities similar to other days within the set of rounds. Since the spin of the cyclical vortex is fractal and holographic in nature, the system of 'time events', though fixed and patterned, is not deterministic but contains infinite levels of accessible information.

From this it follows that there are chronomantic procedures for divining in an oracular manner the different levels of meaning and information from the fixed set of cyclical time events in order to establish ever greater levels of resonance and harmony between the human mind, its sensory ratios and the planetary environment. Were it not for the discovery of the mathematical proofs and demonstrations of the fourth dimension, the topic of chronomancy would be just another theory. Instead, with the understanding and application of the principles of time as the fourth dimension, chronomancy will be established and flourish widely, giving new life to third-dimensional space science which, reconstructed within the whole systems context, will be known as biogeomancy, the science and art of planetary knowing.

Mathematical Principles of Fourth-Dimensional Time

Radial Matrix

The fourth dimension is mathematically constructed as a radial matrix. A radial matrix is a self-existing order of number ratios and harmonics whose units and proportions are generated radially, and of which, in part and in sum, all of the units possess a radial relation to each other. All fourth-dimensional mathematics are radial; all radial matrices are whole number sets. There are no irrational or fractional numbers, but instead simple sets of fractals and ratios whose power of exponential magnification is infinite.

In its formulaic essence the radial matrix is demonstrated as the 0-19 galactic notational code. In this code, as in any radial matrix, there are equal orders of simultaneous sets extending from an infinite and indefinable centerpoint and extending equally in all directions. Each order of sets consists at minimum of two equally extended antipodal orders, and the sums of all sets of antipodal orders, represented by a set of numbers and their subsets independent of the antipodal orders, is equal, e.g. in the 0-19 code, the sum is always 19.

The totality of radial sets of antipodal orders and the number sets from which they are constructed is referred to as a matrix, the underlying self-generated order of time as the fourth dimension. Because the mathematical description of the matrix underlying order of the fourth dimension is radiative and reciprocally self-informing in all its parts, time cannot properly be conceived of as linear, nor can it be said to have any beginning or end point.

Fractals

Fourth-dimensional radial mathematical constructs describing energetic and informational transformations are purely fractal in nature, even where types of geometry are involved. Fractals are self-existing, holographic and infinitely scalar, maintaining their proportions over any magnitude of scale. Fractals are to the fourth dimension what geometry is to the third dimension. For third-dimensional science there is no space without matter and energy; however, time has always been open to question, for as Vernadsky points out, 'time is not a dimension of metric geometry'.

Third-dimensional space-matter science is built up of geometries which describe a world of solids of varying degrees of complexity, while algebraic equations are used to describe the energetic transformations of the different elemental states spanning the ever-changing world of the solids. Time cannot be described in this way, nor can it really be said to be described vectorally.

However, from the perspective of the fourth dimension, space may either be an infinitely locatable point, or a single point supplied by an infinitesimal vector. The single point in space conforms to the now moment for any number of infinite orders of being capable of experiencing the now at any given point in space. This infinitely locatable point of space may be informed by series of fractals whose proportions yield different forms of information. This information is in the nature of interactive timing frequencies. The timing frequencies are results of different levels of ratio downloads which are understood as information governing different stages of evolutionary whole systems change.

The fractal series available to any given moment or set of moments pertaining to the infinitely locatable point in space are always dependent on variables of evolutionary stage, mental development and self-reflective awareness.

From this two corollaries are to be drawn: timing frequencies and time itself are understandable only from a whole systems approach; and until there is a self-reflective capacity of mental development, the science of time cannot be properly elaborated upon. Conversely, the entrainment of mind to the nature of the fourth-dimensional matrix and the fractals which are facilitated by this matrix open the mind to its further evolution. In other words, we cannot speak of timing frequencies and the fractals of time without speaking of the mind's evolutionary advancement.

The timing frequencies themselves, in relation to the phenomena of the third dimension, are holographically inclusive and extend from larger and more inclusive levels of order to lesser levels of order. Though it is a truism to speak of the inseparability of space and time, or of the space-time continuum, in truth time is the ordering principle of space, and only as the container of space (and not vice versa) can it be said to be inseparable from space. Though in no way can time be described from the exclusive formulae of third-dimensional science and mathematics, fourth-dimensional mathematics can supply new synthesizing levels of understanding for dealing with the matter-energy permutations of third-dimensional space (see below: Pulsars).

In fourth-dimensional order a number is not a quantitative function but a qualitative composite, a precise intersection of fractal possibilities whose different harmonic and chromatic textures open the mind to its own sensorium. The different fractal ratios of fourth-dimensional time consist of moving sums of number relations. The resonant interaction of these moving number relations constitutes the palpable mental medium of the radial matrix. The different sets of fractal ratios nested infinitely within each other define the equally infinite levels of creative order unceasingly generated by the matrix.

The key fourth-dimensional fractal unit is known as the

wavespell, which is defined as a self-existing 13-unit (kin) cosmology. The key number units involved in the constituent creation of the 13-kin wavespell are: 4, a composite of the first three orders of number, which establishes the self-existing order; 5 (4+1), which brings in the overtone power of the g-force; and 13 (4+5+4), which is the cosmic tone informing the fifth; between the fifth (4+1) and the thirteenth (9+4) orders is the 8, the logarithmic fractal interval between the 5 and the 13 (5+3=8, 8+5=13), Hence the key wavespell ratio: 5:8 :: 8:13 (see below: Wavespell).

Ratios

Just as the geometries of the third dimension yield descriptions of solids in all of their energetic fluctuations, even if these solids are merely sub-atomic particles, so the fractals of the fourth dimension yield different sets of ratios which inform the timing frequencies at all levels of operation. The ratios are dependent upon and coordinated by the number orders of the radial matrix, and provide the informative content of the different fractals. Ultimately, the ratios describe both the different capacities of the timing frequencies and the sensory orders of human experience.

The mathematical ratios whose proportions remain constant across scale create fractal equivalences with themselves in different magnitudes of scale or with other sets of ratios. In the wavespell example, the constituent ratio, 5:8 :: 8:13, remains constant whether the kin unit of the wavespell is the equivalent of a day, a moon, a year etc. Like number, all ratios are mental in nature and are complemented or augmented by analogical orders of metaphor. Just as mind is the sub- and superstratum of reality, so the fourth dimension is the sub- and superstratum of the third dimension.

The mental order or condition of time is no less real or unreal than the traditional solid, liquid and gaseous states of the third dimension. As a mental order, time and the fourth dimension are an all-encompassing and all-permeating state or condition, superseding the physiochemical liquid, solid and gaseous states, while informing the full spectrum of electromagnetic energy transitions perceptible as the third dimension. In other words, as the sum of the ratio expressions of the galactic mental order, time is in actuality the origin of the third-dimensional physiochemical changes, their agent of transmutation, and their noospheric transformational conclusion.

In the full development of the pulsar science of the wavespell in all of its ratio permutations is to be found the full fourth-dimensional complement of the third-dimensional biophysical and geochemical sciences. The 'scale' of ratios is provided by the 'Harmonic Index' which displays the full range of the 260-kin permutations defining the galactic interdimensional enzymes, as well as the 32 binary sets of harmonics by which time as galactic biology orders itself into a self-organizing system of four-unit microwholes called harmonics.

The Tetrahedron and Tetrahedral Order

The tetrahedron, the primal geometric form found naturally in crystalline states, is the agent of information and energy transductions between the third and fourth dimensions. From the fourth dimension the tetrahedron facilitates ratio energy transduction into third-dimensional quanta; from the third dimension, the tetrahedron facilitates the transduction of quantum information into fourth-dimensional energy, which is spectral rather than material in nature. Fourth-dimensional spectral phenomena are characterized by form and luminosity but lack volume and mass.

As the formal organizing unit of the fourth dimension, the structure of the tetrahedron underlies and informs the wavespell's ratios and pulsar 'geometries'. To each of the four points of the tetrahedron correspond the first, fifth, ninth and thirteenth positions of the wavespell. The unity in time of these four wavespell positions conditions the fourth-dimensional properties of the tetrahedron. The three remaining sets of three units each of the wavespell establish three interactive, triangular planes of time joined by a common point. This point is the invisible fifth or 'plus one' center point of the interior of the tetrahedron from which extend four vertices ending at each of the tetrahedron's four visible points. This center point also represents the g-force ratio conduit between the infinitely locatable point of third-dimensional space — the now — and the higher fourth- and fifth-dimensional orders of galactic time and mind.

Tetrahedral order refers to the use of the tetrahedron in the description and construction of other holon forms, for example the icosahedral planet holon. In actuality all classic geometrical forms are tetrahedral derivatives; likewise the core and structure of the Earth as a solid are crystalline in origin and in the nature of a complex tetrahedral order. Just as the ultimate geometrical reduction of quanta is a tetrahedron, so the minimum condensation of fourth-dimensional information is also a tetrahedron. As the sum of all formal geometrical possibilities, the sphere contains the tetrahedron at its core.

The Plus One Factor

The plus one (+1) factor is the mathematical principle of the recirculation of time as a spiral vortex. Without the plus one factor, there would be a flat stasis, a constantly re-recorded musical score with a forgotten beginning and an unwanted ending, at best resolved into the kind of hopelessly complex entropic order which third-dimensional human civilization now exhibits. The plus one factor transforms a moving orbit on a flat plane in space into a vortex in time.

Plus one represents the overtone power of the g-force (4+1). In terms of relativity, the formula for time is stated: $T=f (E=MC^2 +1)$. Time is a function of the speed of light plus one; properly put, light is overtoned by time. By bringing in the overtone, the interdimensional g-force resonance, the plus one factor places any third-dimensional phenomenon measurable by third-dimensional instrumentation, even light, into its immeasurable and intangible fourth-dimensional condition where mutation is a realizable option.

In the dot-bar galactic 0-19 code, the plus one factor is represented as the passage from the four dot equivalence of the number four, or the order of the fourth, to the bar equivalence of five or the order of the fifth. In the color formula of the time harmonics, red-white-blue-yellow, the plus one factor yields the fifth color, green, resulting in a fifth time cell. In the tetrahedron, the three sides automatically create a plus one, the fourth side; while the four points tacitly proceed from a fifth interior point, the plus one factor holding the tetrahedron together.

The plus one factor is the power of time to transmute complex forms beyond their point of entropic stasis. While 12 is a complex number of a crystalline yet static perfection, plus one yields 13, the prime number representing the galactic power of the vortical recirculation of time. Likewise the 32 sets of binary Harmonics yield 64, matching the set of 64 DNA codons, which like the complex 12, yields a stasis; 64 plus one, the unpaired 33rd Harmonic, yields 65 (13 x 5), representing the interdimensional power of the g-force to invigorate the corpus of living matter beyond itself into its next evolutionary stage.

Thirteen perfect moons of 28 days each yields 364. Like 12, 32 and 64, 364 is an even more complex number also represented as 52 x 7, the number of weeks in a solar year; 364 plus one, green day, which is outside of the days of the calendar, yields 365 (5 x 73), the number of whole days in the Earth's solar orbit, thus assuring the 13-moon cycle the power of vortical recirculation. This power of recirculation is demonstrated by the fact that the solar-galactic year follows the ever-changing harmonic sequence of red, white, blue and yellow years.

In Sum: The mathematical principles of the fourth dimension governing time and the timing frequencies of orders of whole systems are:

i)   radial, hence consisting of radically non-linear, harmonic sets of matching whole number patterns operating as

ii)   a matrix, a self-existing and self-generating whole number construct whose power of movement is

iii) fractal, whole number configurations capable of symmetrical consistency across scale; fractals are constructed of

iv)   ratios, which bear information through sets of constant proportions;

v)   the tetrahedron is the minimal geometrical form with maximum information-bearing capacity; while

vi)   the plus one factor resolves all stasis and assures continuous recirculation of information as a vortex continuum without beginning or end.

Mathematical Proofs and Demonstrations

The 0-19 Code

The proofs and demonstrations of the mathematics of fourth-dimensional time are derived from the self-existing 0-19 code. The dot-bar notational system intrinsic to this code is vigesimal, dynamically iconic, and through use of a zero value, exponentially flexible — that is, advancing in positions whose value increases by the power of 20. Thus, in the first position a dot equals one unit or kin, while a bar equals five; in the second position each dot equals 20 units or kin, while each bar equals 100; in the third, each dot equals 400, each bar 2000; in the fourth position a dot equals 8000 kin; in the fifth each dot equals 160,000 kin and so on.

Arabic numerals are non-iconic, literal notations whose power is conceptually limited. For example, a one-to-one translation of a value from dot-bar notation to Arabic is only approximate, a single-valued literal notation never capable of conveying the multi-valued power of a graphic iconic notation. The patterns of the 0-19 code demonstrate the multivalued power of the iconic notation system, i.e. note that the horizontal rows possess a unity through dot equivalences, while the vertical rows possess unity of bar equivalences (see: 0-19 Galactic Notation, page 42. Also Kwik Reference Card, Dreamspell kit).

All of the constructs and proofs derived from this vigesimal dot-bar notational code also take the form of self-existing mathematical orders or structures. Empirically manifest as the different parts and tools of the Dreamspell kit, the mathematical demonstrations exist as a novel unity for human experience at this time.

Ultimate verification of these mathematical proofs can come about only through an adjustment of human behavior to the fourth-dimensional norms and codes of galactic time. Such an act of behavioral adjustment constitutes a free will choice and level of intelligence that opens into a vast evolutionary momentum. This is the evolutionary momentum that registers the transition of the biosphere into the noosphere, the movement of human consciousness from third-dimensional entropy to the galactic order of mind and being. This is why the application of the key forms of the fourth-dimensional mathematical demonstrations are virtual recipes for autonomous self and whole systems reorganization through the power of time.

The Wavespell

The wavespell is the standard fractal unit of measure. In the term wavespell, wave refers to the power of movement, spell to the power one can gain by being in harmony with reality. Hence, to know and to ride a wavespell is to demonstrate augmented autonomous power through harmonic identification with fourth-dimensional time.

A wavespell is a fractal form-constant of 13 units. These 13 units represent a fourth-dimensional, 13-tone cosmology. In the fourth-dimensional cosmology the 13 constituent units cannot be separated and understood apart from each other. The units are referred to as tones because the nature of the fourth-dimensional reality is purely vibrational, spectral and weightless. Hence each tone represents a discrete cosmological sequence which describes a process of on-going creation. While each of the 13 positions holds the value of one kin, the value of each tone represents a creative power of resonance, each power building on the previous tone or sum of preceding tones (see: Adventure Wavespell, page 55 and back of Oracle Board, Dreamspell kit).

In the whole systems approach, the planetary level represents the minimum whole system; the unit kin represents one rotation of the planet on its axis. Since all elements of the planet from core to magnetosphere turn simultaneously together and interdependently on the same axis, one kin value incorporates the planetary whole system in all of its multitudinous components through one axial turn. For this reason, the minimum kin value is one day-and-night, and the minimum wavespell value of 13 kin is the same as 13 days or 13 full rotations of Earth upon her axis. By fractal expansion, where one kin equals 28 days, then one wavespell equals 13 moons, or 364 (28 x 13) rotations of Earth upon her axis.

This means that through conscious attunement to the wavespell the self-reflective component of the planetary system, the noosphere, will recapitulate in unceasing waves the 13-tone cosmology

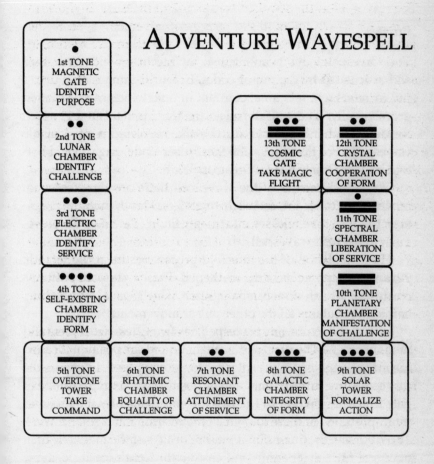

ADVENTURE WAVESPELL

1st TONE
MAGNETIC
GATE
IDENTIFY
PURPOSE

2nd TONE
LUNAR
CHAMBER
IDENTIFY
CHALLENGE

3rd TONE
ELECTRIC
CHAMBER
IDENTIFY
SERVICE

4th TONE
SELF-EXISTING
CHAMBER
IDENTIFY
FORM

13th TONE
COSMIC
GATE
TAKE MAGIC
FLIGHT

12th TONE
CRYSTAL
CHAMBER
COOPERATION
OF FORM

11th TONE
SPECTRAL
CHAMBER
LIBERATION
OF SERVICE

10th TONE
PLANETARY
CHAMBER
MANIFESTATION
OF CHALLENGE

5th TONE
OVERTONE
TOWER
TAKE
COMMAND

6th TONE
RHYTHMIC
CHAMBER
EQUALITY OF
CHALLENGE

7th TONE
RESONANT
CHAMBER
ATTUNEMENT
OF SERVICE

8th TONE
GALACTIC
CHAMBER
INTEGRITY
OF FORM

9th TONE
SOLAR
TOWER
FORMALIZE
ACTION

of the fourth dimension. This is why the wavespell is referred to as a recapitulative and recombinant cosmology, and also as the primary template for evolutionary advancement provided by the codes of fourth-dimensional time. To understand the wavespell in its entirety is to reconstitute the epistemological bases and categorizations of human knowing.

Pulsars

The wavespell exhibits an intrinsic architecture which is defined and articulated by the pulsar codes. In fourth-dimensional time a pulsar refers to a relational constant in time which can be plotted geometrically. The pulsar codes are the mechanism by which dynamic exchanges occur during the momentum of a single wavespell. (For this discussion see: Pulsar Code, page 58 and bottom back of Oracle Board, Dreamspell kit).

In the architecture of the wavespell there are three essential movements: tones 1-4, establish; tones 5-8, extend; tones 9-12, convert; the 13th tone releases into 'magic flight', i.e. takes the movement to the next wavespell.

The articulation of the threefold process occurs at the 1st, 5th, 9th and 13th moments of the wavespell. These four tonal positions create the fourth-dimensional pulsar which, as a tetrahedron, enfolds or contains all the other pulsar movements.

In its architecture, any wavespell has two gates, two towers and nine chambers. The first tone is magnetic and the position is called the magnetic gate; it is the entrance to the wavespell. Likewise, the thirteenth tone is the cosmic, and its position creates the cosmic exit gate from the wavespell. The two towers are held by the fifth and ninth positions and are known as the overtone and solar towers. Thus, the fourth-dimensional pulsar consists of the magnetic first, overtone fifth, solar ninth and cosmic thirteenth tonal positions which are the wavespell's towers and gates.

Being of time and the mind, the fourth-dimensional time pulsar unifies purpose through command, formalized action and magic flight. The time pulsar also informs and regulates the other three pulsars, which constitute three interactive, triangular planes. The activity of these three interactive triangular planes is referred to as the third dimension or physical plane of reality. In actuality these three pulsars comprise the first three dimensions, which function nonetheless as a single whole and which cannot be considered apart from the fourth-dimensional tetrahedron-pulsar which informs and contains them all. Study of the fourth-dimensional pulsar is serviced by the new art and science of chronomancy (see above).

Between the magnetic gate and the overtone tower, the overtone tower and the solar tower, and the solar tower and the cosmic gate, are three sequences of chambers. Each set of three chambers in sequence forms a pulsar. In this way each pulsar has a tonal unit in each of the three wavespell phases: the (galactic) establishment, the (solar) extension and the (planetary) conversion.

In sequential order, the three chambers immediately following the fourth-dimensional magnetic gate and the two towers constitute the first-dimensional lunar life pulsar. The first-dimension lunar life pulsar includes: the second chamber or lunar tone; the sixth chamber or rhythmic tone; and the tenth chamber or planetary tone. The first-dimension lunar life pulsar encompasses the entire realm of biogeochemical changes, which can now be studied or comprehended as the realm of geobiology.

The second or middle position of the three sets of chambers constitutes the second-dimension electric sense pulsar. The second-dimensional pulsar includes: the third chamber or electric tone; the seventh chamber or resonant tone; and the eleventh chamber or spectral tone. The second-dimension sense pulsar encompasses the entire psychophysical realm of electrosensory thresholds, which can now be studied or comprehended as the realm of art and physics.

The third or final aggregate of the three sets of chambers, occupying the positions immediately preceding the two fourth-dimensional towers and the cosmic gate, constitutes the third-dimension self-existing mind pulsar. The third-dimensional pulsar includes: the fourth chamber or self-existing tone; the eighth chamber or galactic tone; and the twelfth chamber or crystal tone. The third-dimension mind pulsar encompasses the realm of mental and social development, which can now be studied or comprehended as the realm of cooperative cosmic order.

The overtone pulsars comprise a second set of pulsars. The

PULSAR CODE

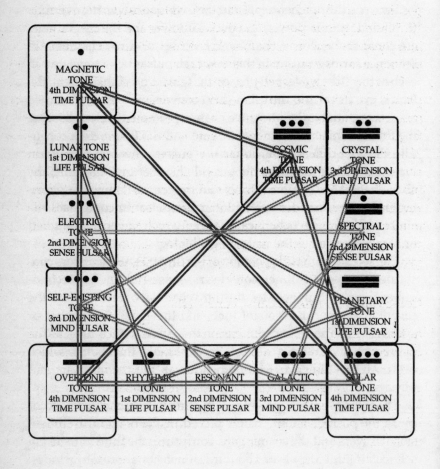

overtone pulsars are moved by the power of the overtone fifth, which in its essence is a function of the plus one factor and the dotbar code (see above). For any wavespell this means that there is a one dot pulsar, including tonal positions 1, 6 and 11; a two dot pulsar, inclusive of tonal positions 2, 7 and 12; a three dot pulsar, including tonal positions 3, 8 and 13; a four dot pulsar, connecting tonal positions 4 and 9; and a bar pulsar, connecting tonal positions 5 and 10. While the four pulsars themselves define the synchronically interconnected realms of the four dimensions, the overtone pulsars provide cross-dimensional time structures.

Between the tonal positions, gates, towers or chambers of the pulsars are 15 vertices which in their connections define all of the possible relations of the tones to each other in their dimensional frequencies. Between the tonal positions of the overtone pulsars are 11 vertices. The combined number of pulsar and overtone pulsar vertices animating the inner dynamics of the 13-tone wavespell is precisely 26 (13 x 2) (see end pages). Study of the 26 tonal relation vertices is fundamental to the development of interdimensional mind technologies whose capacity for reformulating events in time could prove most helpful in dealing with the deleterious effects of toxic waste, radioactivity and diseases like AIDS and Cancer.

Color Cube, Harmonics and Time Cells

In fourth-dimensional time, harmonic refers to a recurring four-color code constant: red, white, blue, yellow. The four-color code constant is literally harmonic because the set includes the three primary color values — red-yellow-blue — from which all secondary values are derived; and white, which is the full spectrum composite of all prismatic values. The four colors in combination establish three fundamental sets of relations: antipodal, analog and occult.

Red and blue, and white and yellow form the two sets of antipodal relations; red and white, and blue and yellow form the two sets of analog relations; and red and yellow, and white and blue form the two pairs of occult relations. These six relational pairs — twelve color units in all — are geometrically constructed as a color cube or galactic time atom, where the top and bottom faces exhibit in paired triangles the two antipode relations; the front and back sides exhibit in paired triangles the two analog relations; and the two lateral sides exhibit in paired triangles the two occult relations. Any of the eight points of the cube exhibit a meeting of six color triangulations. Four of the points represent a dominant color juncture, where three same-colored triangulations meet: the other four points become an optical illusion, showing three sides of a tetrahedron, the 'invisible side' being the color missing from that triangulation point. (See: Color Cube, page 61 and Dreamspell kit.)

Each of the four contiguous lateral walls of the interior of the color cube exhibit each of the four color constants in counterclockwise order, beginning with red on the right, then white facing, blue to the left, and yellow opposite the white. The floor of the color cube is the secondary color green, representing the overtone fifth and introducing the principle of the chromatic, which is the same as the bar in the dot-bar notation (see below). The inside top of the color cube depicts the galactic time atom demonstrated in the directional arrangement where red is east and on the right, blue is west and on the left, white is north and above, and south is yellow and below; with green holding the center.

In temporal sequence, each color holds the minimum value of one kin. One four-color-coded sequence constitutes the value of one harmonic. When the four colors are combined in repeating sequence with the 0-19 code, a harmonic run is created in which there are five time cells, each time cell being one complete four-color-coded harmonic, Within one harmonic run of five time cells, each of the 20 values of the 0-19 code acquires a harmonically coded color constant: code numbers 1, 5, 9, 13 and 17 are red; code numbers 2, 6, 10, 14 and 18 are white; 3, 7, 11, 15 and 19 are blue; and 4, 8, 12, 16 and 20 (=0) are yellow. From this it follows that there are four 'color families' of five units each. Each color is associated with an instructional verb, the composite set of which demonstrate the nature of the harmonic action in time: red, initiates; white, refines; blue, transforms; and yellow, ripens.

Each time cell then consists of a sequence of four color-coded numbers of the 0-19 code. In galactic notation the color-coded numbers are known as codespell numbers (see: back of Solar Seal Chips). The five time cells in sequence create a galactic information loop: time cell one, input: inform; time cell two, store: remember; time

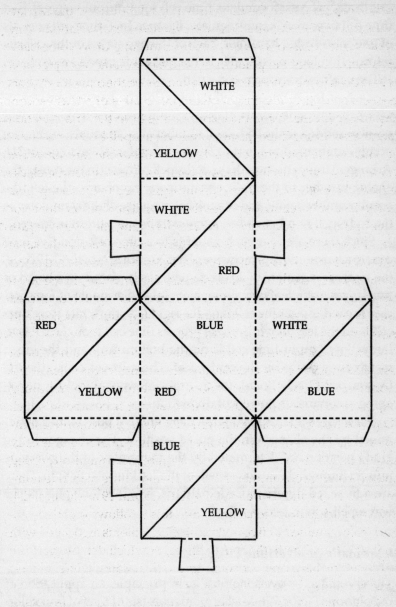

One side of flattened-out

COLOR CUBE

cell three, process: formulate; time cell four, output: express; and time cell five, matrix: self-regulate. Because each time cell consists of one color-coded harmonic, each of the five stages of the galactic information loop participates in the harmonic process as well, i.e. initiate, refine, transform and ripen.

Each of the 0-19 codespell numbers of the harmonic run possesses an antipode number (always a difference of ten); an analog number (added to the codespell number always equals 19); and an occult number (added to the codespell number always equals 21). Arranged as a pattern with the codespell number in the center, the analog number to the right, the antipode number to the left, the occult number below, and a blank color square of the same color as the codespell number above, a five-part oracle pattern is created.

Since there are four such patterns to a time cell, and five time cells to a harmonic run, inclusive of the 20 numbers of the 0-19 code, the total arrangement of 20 oracle patterns is placed on a board of five leaves, each leaf containing a complete harmonic of four oracles: the red input time cell is on the right leaf; the white store time cell is on the leaf above; the blue process time cell is on the left leaf; the yellow output time cell is on the bottom leaf; and the green matrix time cell is on the center leaf. These leaves constitute the Dreamspell Oracle Board, the fourth-dimensional tool for developing autonomous powers of divination.

For each of 20 oracle patterns there are five possibilities determined by the changes in the guide position. The changes in the guide position are determined by the movement of the overtone pulsars through the 20 wavespells of the 260 kin galactic spin. There are a hundred different oracle patterns, five overtone pulsars per wavespell, a hundred per spin.

Chromatic or Overtone Fifth

The chromatic or overtone fifth is, in principle, an application of the plus one factor. While a harmonic consists of a set of four color-coded units in sequence, the base chromatic is a five-color-coded sequence, where the first and fifth units are the same color, and the base chromatic codespell sequence runs: bar, one dot, two dot, three dot, four dot. Within the matrix of the 0-19 code there are four chromatics of five units each (4 x 5 = 20), which are demonstrated as the four vertical columns of the 0-19 code. Because each chromatic spans in whole or in part two time cells, the five-kin chromatic represents the power of circulation. This power of circulation is referred to as 'overtone' because the fifth tone is always the same color value as the first tone; hence, the fifth always overtones the first. Because the movement of harmonics and chromatics is polysynchronous, the principle of movement and circulation is guaranteed.

Because of the overtone fifth, there are five and not four time cells. In the galactic information loop, the fifth time cell assures that the matrix overtone self-regulates and synchronizes during the interval between the output and the next input. In the 13-tone cosmology of the wavespell, the fifth position is the overtone tower marking the transition between the establishment of the self-existing form of the g-force and its extension toward the ninth position of the solar tower. A vertex from the fifth position of the wavespell connects the overtone tower with the thirteenth position, the cosmic gate. The interval between the fifth and the thirteenth is eight, the octave ratio which completes the wavespell ratio, 5:8 :: 8:13.

Moved by the power of the 13, the five time cells yield the 65 Harmonics of the galactic spin, demonstrated as the Dreamspell Journey Board, the Harmonic Index, the Galactic Compass and the Book of Kin (see below). In order for the time cell harmonics to complete the galactic cosmology, each of the four codespell numbers within a time cell acquires an iconic emblem called a solar seal. The icons are called solar seals because the 20 frequencies of the 0-19 code refer to the planet-generating fourth-dimensional solar frequency cycle of 20-kin. This 20-kin cycle seals the chronosphere during each orbital rotation of the planet system Earth, kin after kin, in an unending sequence of Harmonic Runs. The 'names' of the solar seals in sequence recapitulate a multidimensional evolutionary cosmology describing a universal and easily comprehensible memory loop.

According to time cell function the five sets of four solar seals are as shown on page 64.

In combination with each of the 13 tones of the recapitulative cosmology of the wavespell, the 20 solar seals create the 260 kin or

Red Time Cell One: Inform Input
Oracle Board Red Leaf

Red Dragon	initiates input	codespell 1
White Wind	refines input	codespell 2
Blue Night	transforms input	codespell 3
Yellow Seed	ripens input	codespell 4

White Time Cell Two: Remember Store
Oracle Board White Leaf

Red Serpent	initiates store	codespell 5
White World-Bridger	refines store	codespell 6
Blue Hand	transforms store	codespell 7
Yellow Star	ripens store	codespell 8

Blue Time Cell Three: Formulate Process
Oracle Board Blue Leaf

Red Moon	initiates process	codespell 9
White Dog	refines process	codespell 10
Blue Monkey	transforms process	codespell 11
Yellow Human	ripens process	codespell 12

Yellow Time Cell Four: Express Output
Oracle Board Yellow Leaf

Red Skywalker	initiates output	codespell 13
White Wizard	refines output	codespell 14
Blue Eagle	transforms output	codespell 15
Yellow Warrior	ripens output	codespell 16

Green Time Cell Five: Self-Regulate Matrix
Oracle Board Green Leaf

Red Earth	initiates matrix	codespell 17
White Mirror	refines matrix	codespell 18
Blue Storm	transforms matrix	codespell 19
Yellow Sun	ripens matrix	codespell 20 (=0)

= One Complete Harmonic Run

galactic enzymes of the galactic spin. Each fourth-dimensional galactic enzyme consists of an intersection of three frequencies: one of four colors, one of 20 codespell icons, and one of 13 tones. The 260 galactic enzymes are 'cataloged' in the 13 harmonic runs of the Harmonic Index and, through the 65 harmonics of the Book of Kin, are transcribed as the 260 galactic signatures autonomously available to each human who elects to become a planetary kin and enter the noospheric realm of galactic citizenship.

Galactic Spin

When the 20 units of the 0-19 mathematical code are run in a continuing sequence of harmonic runs extended across the fractal unit of the wavespell, the result is the 260-unit (20 x 13) galactic spin, the complete description of the vortical movement of galactic time. The fractal result of this overlay of 13 tones and 20 solar seals (codespell icons) is the complete demonstration of the 13:20 frequency: a 13-unit wavespell repeated 20 times in five sequences of four wavespells each.

The pattern of four wavespells per one of five sequences is a fractal overtone of four solar seals per one of five time cells. For any one of the five sets, each of the four wavespells is chromatically coded by one each of the four colors of the harmonic order: red, white, blue and yellow. All told, there are five red wavespells where the first, fifth, ninth and thirteenth positions are red; five white wavespells where the first, fifth, ninth and thirteenth positions are white; five blue wavespells where the first, fifth, ninth and thirteenth positions are blue; and five yellow wavespells where the first, fifth, ninth and thirteenth positions are yellow.

While the harmonic fourth moved by the chromatic fifth (principle of time cell generation) yields the 20 destiny patterns of the Oracle Board, the same harmonic fourth times the chromatic fifth yields the 20 wavespells of the galactic spin mapped as the five castles of the Dreamspell Journey Board. Castles are to time cells what the 20 wavespells are to the 20 solar seals (codespell icons).

Like the Oracle Board, the Journey Board opens up as five leaves. Each of the five leaves represents one each of the five castles of time. Each of the five 52-kin, four-wavespell fractals of the galactic spin is a perfect Journey Board fifth, a complete, inviolable harmonic architecture called a castle. Just as the wavespell possesses its dynamic tonal architecture, so four wavespells recapitulating the four harmonic color constants create the four directional quarters which constitute the perfect architecture of a castle of time. Each castle consists of 52 kin, 13 harmonics and four wavespells, and is a perfect fractal of every other castle.

Five castles of 52 kin spinning in a common vortical circuit yield the 260 permutations of the 13:20 timing frequency. Each of the 260 positions of the five castles of the Journey Board is a galactic gateway representing one each of the 260 possible entries from the fourth-dimensional order of reality into the third-dimensional sensorium called the physical body or space suit, and which are recorded in the Book of Kin as one of the corresponding 260 Galactic Signatures. The 260 positions of the Journey Board account for every permutation of one of the 20 solar icons with one of the 13 galactic tones and four harmonic colors of creation. Time is biology. The unique triple frequency coding occurs kin after kin, day after day, assuring the planetary whole system a daily evolutionary imprint.

The color and quality of the five castles of time follow the order of the four harmonic color constants plus one, the overtone fifth. While the color movement of the time cells in relation to each other creates a galactic bio-solar information loop, the color movement of the five castles in relation to each other creates a bio-galactic evolutionary information loop. The bio-galactic information loop describes an evolutionary journey in time through whose five stages the nature of galactic being turns, crosses, burns, gives and enchants. Each vortical turn of the bio-galactic evolutionary information loop of the galactic spin recapitulates, as a whole fractal, an ongoing cosmogenesis.

At its minimum information level, the galactic spin imprints the planetary chronosphere every 260 days with the five-part genesis information loop of the five castles. As a complete fractal description of the 13:20 frequency, the Journey Board can be used to map larger fractal time equivalences, for example where one kin may equal a solar year, each castle then represents 52 years, and the entire Journey Board 260 years (counting back from AD 2013). Or, one kin may equal 20 solar years, a castle 1040 solar years, and the Journey

Board 5200 solar years; or, one kin may equal one hundred solar years, a castle 5200 solar years, and the Journey Board 26,000 years, etc.

As with the Oracle Board, on the Journey Board the Red Eastern Castle of Turning is on the right leaf, the White Northern Castle of Crossing is on the upper leaf, the Blue Western Castle of Burning is on the left-hand leaf, the Yellow Southern Castle of Giving is on the lower leaf and the Green Central Castle of Enchantment is on the middle leaf. Within each of these castles are four-color-coded wavespells. Each wavespell sequence describes the inner workings of a specific castle in the creation of the ongoing cosmogenesis. According to color harmonic, castle function, and journey coded by the yellow solar seal in the self-existing position of the red wavespell, the five castles of four wavespells are given on page 68.

When each kin of the galactic spin equals a hundred years or a Dreamspell century, then the 20 wavespells of the Journey Board map out the 26,000 years (260 centuries) of the current evolutionary spiral in which the subcorpus human has risen to dominate the corpus of living matter constituting the organic biosphere component of whole system Earth. This 20-wavespell 26,000-year evolutionary journey is referred to as the 'Dreamspell Genesis', in which each wavespell accounts for 1,300 years, and the entire genesis is divided into three parts, according to the descending evolutionary ratio 5:3 :: 3:2, where the unit '5' represents the first ten wavespells or 13,000 years of the Dragon Genesis, the unit '3' represents the next six wavespells or 7,800 years of the Monkey Genesis; and the unit '2' represents the last four wavespells or 5,200 years of the Moon Genesis. The culminating point of the evolutionary Dreamspell Genesis is pinpointed at Kin 164, Yellow Galactic Seed (July 26) AD 2013. For this reason, the Dreamspell kit of galactic tools is referred to as 'The Journey of Timeship Earth 2013'.

Spectral Fractals

Spectral fractals are a special function of the chromatics applied to the castle structure and demonstrated in the 52-unit four-color-coded 'destiny castle' (see page 70 and right back leaf, Oracle Board, Dreamspell kit) . This formal construct shows the wavespell

Red Eastern Castle of Turning: Court of Birth
Journey Board Red Leaf

Red Dragon   wavespell one   birth initiates turning
White Wizard   wavespell two   timelessness refines turning
Blue Hand   wavespell three   accomplishment transforms turning
Yellow Sun   wavespell four   universal fire ripens turning
        Red Castle initiates seed: through birth seed turns

White Northern Castle of Crossing: Court of Death
Journey Board White Leaf

Red Skywalker   wavespell five   space initiates crossing
White World-Bridger   wavespell six   death refines crossing
Blue Storm   wavespell seven   self-generation transforms
                                                   crossing
Yellow Human   wavespell eight   free will ripens crossing
      White castle refines warrior: through death warrior crosses

Blue Western Castle of Burning: Court of Magic
Journey Board Blue Leaf

Red Serpent   wavespell nine   life-force initiates burning
White Mirror   wavespell ten   endlessness refines burning
Blue Monkey   wavespell eleven   magic transforms burning
Yellow Seed   wavespell twelve   flowering ripens burning
        Blue Castle transforms star: through magic star burns

Yellow Southern Castle of Giving: Court of Intelligence
Journey Board Yellow Leaf

Red Earth   wavespell thirteen   navigation initiates giving
White Dog   wavespell fourteen   heart refines giving
Blue Night   wavespell fifteen   abundance transforms giving
Yellow Warrior wavespell sixteen   intelligence ripens giving
      Yellow Castle ripens sun: through intelligence sun gives

Green Central Castle of Enchantment: Court of the Matrix
Journey Board Central Leaf

Red Moon   wavespell seventeen   universal water initiates
                                             enchantment
White Wind   wavespell eighteen   spirit refines enchantment
Blue Eagle   wavespell nineteen   vision transforms enchantment
Yellow Star   wavespell twenty   elegance ripens enchantment
Green Castle synchronizes human: through matrix human enchants

structure moved by the four colors to create the castle architecture, which is the pure fractal of the vortical movement created by the g-force, the galactic fifth force. The destiny castle has use as a fractal slide-rule of time where each of the 52 units or kin may assume different number values. For instance, if one kin equals seven days, then the destiny castle represents the 52 weeks of the 13-moon solar year, and each wavespell a quarter-year of 13 weeks. Understood as the four-color sequence of any one of the five Earth Families, this fractal structure can be used to plot out any 52-year life or destiny cycle, hence 'destiny castle'.

The most special use of the destiny castle is as a description of the spectral fractal. The spectral fractal describes the 52-chromatic, 260-kin spin which is syncopatedly concurrent with the galactic spin. Just as the five-kin chromatics give the four-kin harmonics their power of movement through the g-force power of circulation, so the spectral fractal 'pulls' the galactic spin through the temporal vortex, rotation after rotation.

The overtone fifth which governs the chromatic is demonstrated in the 1:5 ratio of the one-castle spectral fractal to the five castles of the galactic spin. The spectral fractal is built of 52 kin where each kin has a value of five ($52 \times 5 = 260$). The spectral fractal may be visualized spinning as an overlay on the five castles of the Journey Board. While the 260 kin of the galactic spin plot the fourth-dimensional kin equivalences corresponding to the rotational passage of 260 third-dimensional days, the spectral fractal of 52 chromatics represents a synthesized, purely fourth-dimensional information ratio in resonance with an even more synthesizing fifth-dimensional timing factor.

The fifth-dimensional timing factor is the principle of the four galactic 'seasons' or spectra which describe the primal creative powers of the fifth force. Though each spectrum is mathematically a quarter of the primal timing sequence, from the fourth-dimensional perspective these 'seasons' are perceptible as chromatic runs, each chromatic run being a quarter of an entire chromatic spectrum. As one of the four wavespells of the spectral fractal, each spectral season (spectrum) consists of 13 five-kin chromatics or 65 kin. The fifth-to-fourth-dimensional movement of the four galactic seasons coordinates contiguous fourth-to-third-dimensional galactic spins.

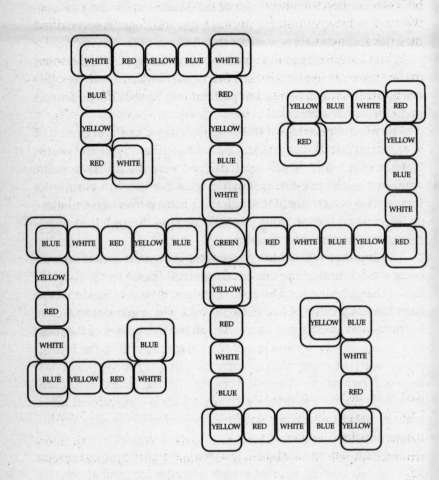

DESTINY CASTLE

It is called a spectral fractal because the pure fourth-dimensional state of reality is spectral (form and luminosity) rather than material (volume and mass). In mathematical terms, the difference between the spectral and material is summed up in the ratio 1:5, where '1' is the synthesized spectral form and '5' the complexified molecular structure.

While the galactic spin is built of a movement of 65 harmonics in combination with the 13 tones of the wavespell, and whereas the harmonic run underlying these harmonics consists of the 20 icons in continuous color-coded rotation from red codespell number 1 (dragon) to yellow codespell number 20 (=0) (sun), the sequence of 52 spectral fractal chromatics begins with yellow codespell 20 (=0) (sun) and ends with blue codespell 19 (storm).

The chromatic is purely a function of the dot-bar movement pattern in which there are four sets of five units each, each unit consisting of the sequence: bar, one dot, two dot, three dot, four dot. Each of these four sets or chromatics represents one each of the powers of the four galactic seasons or spectra, the fifth force timing principle embodied in the spectral fractal. Following the form of the 0-19 notational code, and inclusive of the color-coded solar seals which provide the four chromatics with their overtone, the four chromatics are:

Yellow Sun-Seed Fire Chromatic, basis of Yellow Galactic Spectrum (codespell: 0-4) Season of Ripening, 13 per Spectral Fractal

Red Serpent-Moon Blood Chromatic, basis of Red Galactic Spectrum (codespell: 5-9) Season of Initiating, 13 per Spectral Fractal

White Dog-Wizard Truth Chromatic, basis of White Galactic Spectrum (codespell: 10-14) Season of Refining, 13 per Spectral Fractal

Blue Eagle-Storm Sky Chromatic, basis of Blue Galactic Spectrum (codespell: 15-19) Season of Transforming, 13 per Spectral Fractal

In the 0-19 code the four chromatics create a polar run from bar at the top to four dot at the bottom of the sequence, hence the codespell bar icons or solar seals are referred to as the four 'polar kin' (see: Chromatic Arrangement, page 73 and top back leaf, Journey Board, Dreamspell kit). These four polar kin, Red Serpent (codespell 5), White Dog (codespell 10), Blue Eagle (codespell 15) and

Yellow Sun (codespell 20=0) each articulate the 13-chromatic, 65-kin spectral fractal wavespells of corresponding color into four stages. There are three sequences of 20 kin and four chromatics each, and one of five kin and one chromatic, for a total of 65 kin or 13 chromatics per wavespell. For each set of polar kin in combination with the 13 galactic tones, there are four tones which initiate the four different sequences within one 65-kin wavespell spectrum, which are as follows:

Tone 3 Electric: initiates 20-kin to establish galactic spectrum
Tone 10 Planetary: initiates 20-kin to extend galactic spectrum
Tone 4 Self-existing: initiates 20-kin to convert galactic spectrum
Tone 11 Spectral: initiates 5-kin to transport galactic spectrum

For any wavespell of the spectral fractal, tone 3 initiates the magnetic gate; tone 10 initiates the overtone tower; tone 4 initiates the solar tower; and tone 11 initiates the cosmic gate. Dissynchronous with the 260-kin galactic spin, the spectral fractal literally stitches the galactic spin in the following manner:

65-kin Red galactic spectrum, initiated by Red Serpent, codespell 5 in third (electric) position of Blue Night Wavespell 15 (Yellow Castle).

65-kin White galactic spectrum, initiated by White Dog codespell 10 in third (electric) position of Yellow Star Wavespell 20 (Green Castle).

(New galactic spin always occurs on second kin of third chromatic of first 20-kin phase of white galactic spectrum.)

65-kin Blue galactic spectrum, initiated by Blue Eagle, codespell 15 in third (electric) position of Red Wavespell 5 (White Castle).

65-kin Yellow galactic spectrum, initiated by Yellow Sun codespell 20 in third (electric) position of White wavespell 10 (Blue Castle).

Note that the relation between codespell and wavespell number and solar seal and wavespell color is an antipode constant, i.e. codespell and wavespell numbers are always 10 apart, and colors consistently antipodal red-blue, white-yellow. In this way the spectral fractal demonstrates the equalizing principles of the radial matrix,

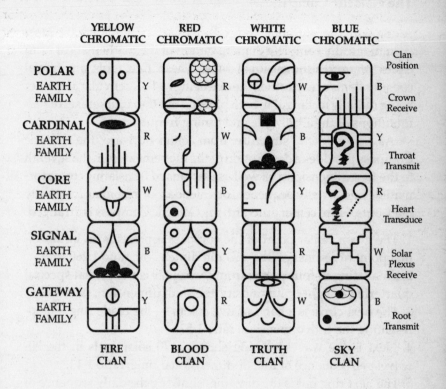

CHROMATIC ARRANGEMENT

Y = Yellow, R = Red, W = White, B = Blue

while entraining the mind in the fifth-to-fourth-dimensional circulatory movement of the g-force.

The Galactic Compass

Along with the Harmonic Index, the Galactic Compass is the most cosmologically complete demonstration of the mathematical principles of fourth-dimensional time. These two tools are fractal coequivalents of each other, the one being radially circular, the other being radially rectangular, both plotting out the complete set of permutations of the 13:20 code and timing frequency.

As a pure fractal structure, from center outward, the Galactic Compass provides a description of the movement from the seventh to the first dimensions, as well as a means of translating this information into a daily sequence, or calendar, of resonant frequency read-outs. From center outward, the Galactic Compass is arranged:

1. The green center point of the compass represents an infinitesimal point of resonance, the seventh dimension; ratio 1:260 (=0).
2. Emanating in four points from the center is the primal spectral quartering of light or luminosity, the sixth dimension; ratio 1:65.
3. The next circle is a band of five colors — the castle ring — representing the fifth dimension; ratio 1:52.
4. Next is the wavespell ring showing 20 solar seals in the 20-wavespell sequence of fourth-dimensional time; ratio 1-13.
5. The next ring out is the day ring, showing the daily sequence of 20 solar seals which create the kin equivalences of third-dimensional time; ratio 1:1.
6. Then comes the 13-tone ring which creates the daily wavespell sequence, and which represents the second electric sense dimension; ratio 1:1.
7. The yellow ring next shows the first-dimensional tonal sequence as a solar periodicity wave; ratio 1:20.
8. Finally, the outermost green ring translates the solar periodicity wave into 19 sequences: 18 of 20 days each and one of five days, which correlate the cycle of the Earth with its annual orbit around the sun, according to both the Gregorian and the 13-Moon calendars.

Since the Galactic Compass is calibrated to the 13:20 timing

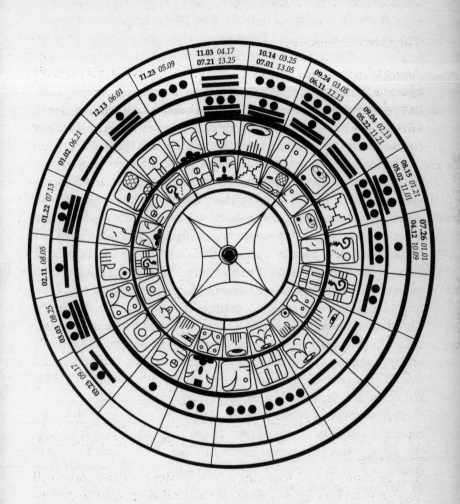

GALACTIC COMPASS

frequency, it is divided into 20 arcs of 18 degrees each. Since the smallest unit of the 13:20 timing frequency is the 260-kin spin, and since this spin consists of only thirteen 20-day sequences, the outermost Green ring runs 13 sequences, then continues its final six sequences of correlate dating directly beneath the compass entry point, 07.26 (July 26 Gregorian = 01.01 first day of the first of the 13 Moons). This means that 260 days later is the spin return point, 04.12 (April 12 Gregorian = 10.09, ninth day of the tenth of the 13 Moons). As of this day, the galactic spin 'repeats' itself, and the kin equivalents of the final six correlate dates match the first six.

The Galactic Compass accounts for 18,980 kin permutation possibilities. These 18,980 kin constitute the galactic cycle of 52 solar years. In other words, it takes the galactic calendar precisely 52 years before one of the 260 galactic signatures falls again on the same day of the 365-day solar cycle. This is demonstrated on the ephemeris on the back of the Galactic Compass. On the outermost edge of the ephemeris are the numbers 1-13 (representing the 13 galactic tones) combined with one of four names, representing the four of 20 solar seals which constitute the Gateway Earth Family. This demonstrates the cycle of 52 galactic gateways (tone and seal) which fall annually on the Gregorian date July 26, or 13-Moon calendar Magnetic Moon, day one. The ephemeris also demonstrates this 52-year periodicity principle for a set of five cycles (AD 1754-2013), the 260-year cycle of biospheric transformation.

A similar set of cycles may be plotted for any day of the year, repeated annually in sets of four years. There are five sets coding the days of the year called Earth Families. Each Earth Family is coded as a set of four solar seals having the same number of dots or bar (see above: Destiny Castle, 0-19 Code; also Chromatic Arrangement, pg. 73 andtop leaf Journey Board). The four solar seals which repeat for the first day of the Magnetic Moon represent the four-dot codespell family, called the Gateway. This set of codespell numbers (Red Moon 9, White Wizard 14, Blue Storm 19 and Yellow Seed 4) according to color always completes one of the four chromatics. Any position of the dial at the center of the compass will define one of the five Earth Families, whether on the wavespell ring or the day ring. Through the use of the Galactic Compass any human may begin to translate his or her reality from the third to the fourth dimension and, in this way, actually participate in the transformation of the biosphere into the noosphere.

Harmonic Index

While the Galactic Compass demonstrates the radial order of galactic time in its dimensional ratios to each other as the minimum solar-galactic cycle of 52 Earth-years, the Harmonic Index (see pp 78-9 and Dreamspell kit) is a perfect description of the self-resonant 13:20 timing frequency. As a catalog and a calibrator, the Harmonic Index stores information in a basic 13 x 20 unit grid, where the horizontal lattices are accorded the names and colors of the 20 solar seals in sequence from Red Dragon to Yellow Sun, and the vertical lattices correspond to the 13 harmonic runs created by these 20 icons as they are moved by the 13 galactic tones.

Just as the 20 solar seals are 'rung' once by each of the galactic tones in a pattern that matches the solar periodicity 1:20 ratio yellow tone ring of the Galactic Compass, so the 13 tones run in a sequence of 20 wavespells through the Harmonic Index grid. This repeated sequence of tones 1-13 corresponds to the white 1-13 tone ring of the Galactic Compass being moved 20 times in its 1:1 ratio with the day ring. The harmonic run of 20 solar seals, Dragon-Sun, corresponds to the white day ring of the compass, which is repeated 13 times in 1:1 ratio with the white tone ring of the compass. Wherever '1' appears on the Harmonic Index, it indicates one of the 20 magnetic gates which inaugurate each of the 20 wavespells. The sequence of Magnetic Gate '1' designates on the Harmonic Index corresponds to the Wavespell ring of the Compass, running from Dragon to Star.

Across the top of the Harmonic Index are the designations of the 13 harmonic runs, with kin numbers, 20 per run, to be correlated with the sequence of 260 galactic signatures in the Book of Kin. Color-coded at the top of the Index, from left to right, is the sequence red, white, blue, yellow and green, representing the five castles positioned above their appropriate Harmonic Runs and inclusive of information regarding their color, wavespell numbers, harmonic numbers and kin numbers.

Along the right side of the Index the same color coding (red,

HARMONIC

	RED EASTERN CASTLE OF TURNING KIN 1-52 HARMONICS 1-13 WAVESPELLS 1-4			WHITE NORTHERN CASTLE OF CROSSING KIN 53-104 HARMONICS 14-26 WAVESPELLS 5-8		
	KIN 1-20	21-40	41-60	61-80	81-100	101-120
	1ST HARMONIC RUN	2ND HARMONIC RUN	3RD HARMONIC RUN	4TH HARMONIC RUN	5TH HARMONIC RUN	6TH HARMONIC RUN
HARMONIC	1	6	11	16	21	26
INVERSE	65	60	55	50	45	40
DRAGON	●①	8	2	9	3	10
WING	2	●9	3	10	4	11
NIGHT	3	10	●4	11	5	12
SEED	4	11	5	●12	6	13
HARMONIC	2	7	12	17	22	27
INVERSE	64	59	54	49	44	39
◇ SERPENT	5	12	6	13	●7	①
WORLD BRIDGER	6	13	7	①	8	●2
HAND	7	①	8	2	9	●3
STAR	8	2	9	3	●10	●4
HARMONIC	3	8	13	18	23	28
INVERSE	63	58	53	48	43	38
MOON	9	3	10	●4	11	●5
◇ DOG	10 ◇	4 ◇	11 ◇	5	12	●6
MONKEY	11	5	●12	6	13	●7
HUMAN	12	6	13	●7	①	●8
HARMONIC	4	9	14	19	24	29
INVERSE	62	57	52	47	42	37
SKYWALKER	13	7	①	8	●2	●9
WIZARD	①	8	2	9	3	●10
◇ EAGLE	2	9	3 ◇	10 ◇	4 ◇	●11 ◇
WARRIOR	3	10	4	11	●5	12
HARMONIC	5	10	15	20	25	30
INVERSE	61	56	51	46	41	36
EARTH	4	11	5	●12	6	13
MIRROR	5	12	●6	13	7	①
STORM	6	●13	7	①	8	2
◇ SUN	●7	①	8	2	9	3 ◇

KEY:
- ● LOOM OF 13 MOONS (GAP KIN)
- ◇ POLAR KIN
- ○ MAGNETIC GATE

INDEX

BLUE WESTERN CASTLE OF BURNING KIN 105-156 HARMONICS 27-39 WAVESPELLS 9-12		YELLOW SOUTHERN CASTLE OF GIVING KIN 157-208 HARMONICS 40-52 WAVESPELLS 13-16		GREEN CENTRAL CASTLE OF ENCHANTMENT KIN 209-260 HARMONICS 53-65 WAVESPELLS 17-20			
121-140	141-160	161-180	181-200	201-220	221-240	241-260	
7TH HARMONIC RUN	8TH HARMONIC RUN	9TH HARMONIC RUN	10TH HARMONIC RUN	11TH HARMONIC RUN	12TH HARMONIC RUN	13TH HARMONIC RUN	
31	36	41	46	51	56	61	**TIME CELL ONE** Input Inform (Red)
35	30	25	20	15	10	5	
4	11	5	12	6	13	• 7	
5	12	6	13	7	• ①	8	
6	13	7	①	• 8	2	9	
7	①	8	• 2	9	3	10	
32	37	42	47	52	57	62	**TIME CELL TWO** Store Remember (White)
34	29	24	19	14	9	4	
8	2	• 9	3 ◇	10 ◇	4 ◇	11 ◇	
9	• 3	10	4	11	5	12	
10	• 4	11	5	12	6	13	
11	• 5	• 12	6	13	7	①	
33	38	43	48	53	58	63	**TIME CELL THREE** Process Formulate (Blue)
33	28	23	18	13	8	3	
12	• 6	13	• 7	①	8	2	
13	• 7	①	8	• 2	9	3 ◇	
①	• 8	2	9	• 3	10	4	
2	• 9	3	• 10	4	11	5	
34	39	44	49	54	59	64	**TIME CELL FOUR** Output Express (Yellow)
32	27	22	17	12	7	2	
3	• 10	• 4	11	5	12	6	
4	• 11	5	12	6	13	7	
5	• 12	6	13	7	①	8	
6	13	• 7	①	8	2	9	
35	40	45	50	55	60	65	**TIME CELL FIVE** Matrix Self-Regulate (Green)
31	26	21	16	11	6	1	
7	①	8	• 2	9	3	10	
8	2	9	3	• 10	4	11	
9	3	10	4	11	• 5	12	
10 ◇	4 ◇	11 ◇	5	12	6	• 13	

white, blue, yellow and green) indicates the five time cells, four solar seals in the color sequence red-yellow, within each time cell. Since the four-kin harmonics are based on the time cell, the Harmonic Numbers are listed in sequence, five per Harmonic Run, across the top of each time cell division of the Harmonic Index. Beneath each Harmonic Number is a number in a green band which represents the Harmonic's Inverse Number.

The radial nature of the Harmonic Index is demonstrated in the numerical listing of the Harmonics and their Inverses. Note how the four corners are each other's inverses in a diagonal pattern that is the pure expression of the radial matrix. Note next that the Red and the Green time cells are each other's Inverses, while the White and the Yellow also completely inverse each other. The Blue time cell provides its own inverse patterns. Likewise note that the Blue Castle is made up entirely of its own inverse, while the Red and Green and White and Yellow Castles also harmonically inverse each other.

Note that there are 65 Harmonics, divided into 32 sets of Harmonics and their inverses, each pair of numbers of which adds up to 66 (65+1), and one Harmonic which is its own Inverse, the 33rd Harmonic, the sum of which doubled is also 66. Note the position of the 33rd Harmonic precisely in the center of the central column of the 7th Harmonic Run. Like the Blue Time Cell, and the Blue Western Castle, the Seventh Harmonic Run is its own Inverse, all its harmonics being inversed within itself. Note next that Harmonics and Inverses also pair off according to paired sets of Harmonic Runs: the 1st and the 13th, the 2nd and the 12th, the 3rd and the 11th, the 4th and the 10th, the 5th and the 9th, and the 6th and the 8th. In this way the radial matrix is thoroughly expressed in what otherwise appears as a mere two-dimensional template or permutation table.

Two other patterns are indicated directly on the grid of the Harmonic Index. Beginning top down and moving by fifths are the polar kin: Red Serpent, first fifth; White Dog, second fifth; Blue Eagle, third fifth; and Yellow Sun, fourth fifth. The polar kin are indicated in their 3-10-4-11 positions articulating the three 20-kin and one 5-kin phases of each of the galactic spectra or seasons. Note that the 13th Harmonic Run is split between the last nine kin of the

Serpent season, and the first eleven kin of the Dog season. The completion of the establishment phase of the Dog season is always the first nine days of the next galactic spin. The first 'new season' of any spin always begins with 3 Eagle, wavespell 5 in the third Harmonic Run.

The other pattern indicated in the Harmonic Index is the 'Loom of the 13 Moons'. This pattern indicates a sequence of 52 kin referred to in the Book of Kin as Galactic Activation Portals (GAP days). The Loom of 13 Moons I have also referred to as the 'Loom of Maya' (1987) and the 'Binary Triplet Configuration' (1984). The pattern of this loom is a further demonstration of the power of the radial matrix. In actuality the Loom consists of 13 sets of two pairs of matched kin having an occult color relation to each other, hence called occult quartets. The structure of each quartet creates an equidistant matrix of itself on the Harmonic Index, while the tonal numbers of each of the four positions of any one of these 13 quartets adds up to 28.

Thirteen quartets times 28 produces a tonal sum 364. For this reason this configuration is called the Loom of the 13 Moons, for in the 13-Moon calendar there are 28 days each, for a total of 364 days, less the 'plus one' Green day, which is subsumed as the indefinable point at the center of the 33rd Harmonic. While any set of paired occult icons on the Harmonic Index will yield a pattern whose sum is always 28, the Loom of 13 Moons pattern is distinguished by the elegance of its fractal form, indicating a radial relationship between the orbital circulation of third-dimensional time as a pattern of 364+1 days, and the fourth-dimensional matrix of the 260-kin galactic spin. The relation between the orbital third-dimensional pattern and the radial fourth-dimensional pattern is punctuated by the 52 GAP days. Experiential calibration of the GAP days will reveal further clues regarding the nature of time and the evolutionary transition of the biosphere into the noosphere.

In essence, the Harmonic Index in all of its patterns is a compendium of resonant categories and radial calibration possibilities. It is both a proof and a tool for following the kin registrations upon the planet's chronosphere. As the sum of the registrations of the 13:20 timing frequency, the chronosphere in turn imprints these registrations upon the Psi Bank. As humans elect to assume their galactic

THE 20 SOLAR SEALS

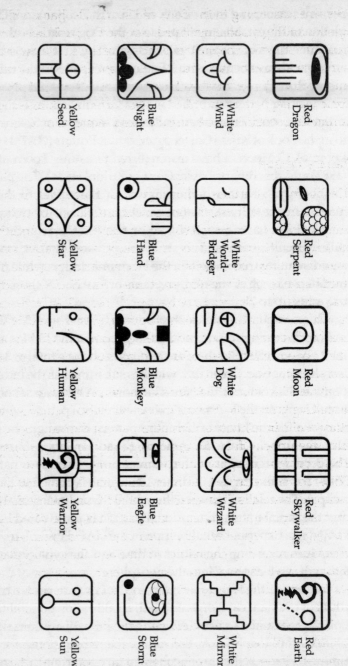

Yellow Seed	Blue Night	White Wind	Red Dragon
Yellow Star	Blue Hand	White World-Bridger	Red Serpent
Yellow Human	Blue Monkey	White Dog	Red Moon
Yellow Warrior	Blue Eagle	White Wizard	Red Skywalker
Yellow Sun	Blue Storm	White Mirror	Red Earth

identities according to the Book of Kin, the Psi Bank will become correspondingly more activated. As the Psi Bank becomes more activated, the chronosphere will self-regulate. As the chronosphere self-regulates, the transition from biosphere to noosphere will approach its climax. It is this climactic moment for which the human form was engineered in order to catalyze the Earth into a realm of luminous consciousness beyond present description.

Binary Pentad

The binary pentad is a special megafractal function of the overtone fifth used to describe: a) the respiratory function of the stellar-planetary whole system design (Galactic Solar 0-19 Code, back left leaf of Journey Board); and b) the progression of biomutational sequences or geneses of the current evolutionary spiral (Dreamspell Genesis, right back leaf of Journey Board). The power of the fifth creates the five turns of the binary pentad. In both cases the binary pentad is a pentagonal structure (five angles, 72 degrees each), which may be viewed as the progression of five perfectly color-coded cells of four units each, and/or as two rings, an outer and an inner ring.

a) Galactic Solar 0-19 Code shows the progression of daily kin according to the 0-19 chromatic sequence coded according to planetary orbits in relation to each other, where the sequence 0-9 goes from the upper left to the upper right on the outside green ring. This represents the galactic movement from the outermost planet, Pluto, to the innermost, Mercury, along with the corresponding codespell numbers. The solar movement from codespell 10 to 19 proceeds on the inner yellow ring in the opposite direction from upper right to upper left. Each pair of codespell numbers on the inner and outer ring constitutes an analog color relationship. This binary pentad describes as a whole system the relation of the planets to each other, both as a daily sequence and as a cosmological whole.

b) Dreamspell Genesis demonstrates virtually the same design: five blocks of four color-coded units each, arranged in two circles, outer and inner. While the Solar-Galactic pentad describes the 1:1 daily sequence, the Genesis pentad describes the 1:13 wavespell sequence. The outer progression runs from Dragon (1) to Mirror (10). The inner ring, following the same movement as the outer ring, describes the progression from Monkey (11) to Star (20). While the outer progression of ten wavespells describes the all-enclosing primary Dragon genesis, the inner progression describes the minimum fractal division of the primary genesis into two secondary geneses, the Monkey and the Moon.

All three geneses have a fractal ratio to each other which describes the descending involutionary order: 10:6 :: 6:4 (5:3 :: 3:2). The descending ratio of involution accounts for the compression of time into space which occurs in the Moon Genesis, where 4=(10+6), or 4=(16)=4 squared. The units of the sets of pairs on the outer and inner rings bear a perfect antipode codespell and color relation to each other. The relation of units to each other and to the whole exhibited by both the Solar-Galactic 0-19 Code and the Dreamspell Genesis constitutes a minimum binary flex (movement in pairs according to inner and outer rings) of the overtone fifth organized as a pentagonal fractal. In this way the binary pentad is a fractal measure of both the 1:1 cosmological order of the stellar-planetary system (analog) and the 1:13 biomutational sequence of 'geneses' (antipode).

Part III

SYNTHESIS AND APPLICATION: THE ADVENT OF THE NOOSPHERE

The synthesis and application of the principles of time from its own dimension are constituted in the program of tools called Dreamspell, the Journey of Timeship Earth 2013. A Dreamspell refers to any agreed-upon consensus reality. From a planetary perspective, a Dreamspell may describe lesser or greater cycles of chronospheric envelopes woven over the Earth's orbital rotation around the sun. Permeated by registrations of the galactic spin, a chronospheric Dreamspell may become reflective in consciousness, attaining a primary order or level of galactic being. This is the evolutionary possibility made available by a correct understanding of time as the fourth dimension, understood and applied as the Dreamspell.

Recognizing the Dreamspell as an evolutionary solution, a set of codes and tools for knowing and mastering time, we have come to terms with the problem which confronted us at the outset of this book: that of humanity's alienation from nature. According to the analysis and critique of time from its own dimension, this problem, which results in spreading social disorder and uncontrollable environmental degradation, is due to an error in time. The creation, fostering and acceptance of the artificial 12:60 timing frequency is the error in time whose very premise takes us farther and farther away from nature without any hope of resolution. To correct this error, to abandon the 12:60 timing frequency, is to open the possibility for a reunion with nature by re-entering the natural 13:20 timing frequency of the whole system Earth.

To hasten this reunion with nature, all that is necessary for a first step is to release ourselves from the 12-month Gregorian calendar and adopt the calendar of the 13 Moons. The 13-Moon calendar is an evolutionary tool to assist humanity in the unprecedented act of uniting itself on one issue central to its complete well-being: time. The harmonic convergence of humanity on this one issue, combined with the inescapable order, perfection and simplicity of following the 13-Moon calendar will lift the species as a simultaneous whole into the galactic timing frequency of 13:20. This evolutionary moment will ensure that the subcorpus human — the leading, destiny-bearing edge of the mass of living planetary matter — has commenced to make conscious the transition of the biosphere into the noosphere. This simple act, adoption of the 13-Moon calendar, in correcting the timing frequency, will be as triumphant a moment as humanity has known for itself. For in this simple act of changing calendars humanity will have restored to itself a level of collective self-esteem long since forgotten. Things undreamed of now will flood the imagination. As humanity goes, so goes the planet. In becoming unified with itself humanity will signal the unification of the planet as a whole system. Instead of alienation from nature, the new order will be synthesis with nature.

Once the 13-Moon calendar is in motion all of humanity will be in the same newly unified standard of equal time. Equality of time will mean the return of science to the people as the Dreamspell galactic tool kit. Through universal promulgation and propagation of this tool kit, every last human will have the opportunity of furthering his or her own self-evolution and entry into galactic culture. Not only will science return to the hands of the people, but so also will an empowerment to live a life of harmonious autonomy and art-full order. In ending the conflict in itself, a conflict brought on and confirmed by an error in time, humanity will end its conflict with nature. A new social order will arise. The arts of peace will flourish as never before. Very rapidly, whole system Earth will be transformed into a living art spore, the fulfillment of the planetization of humankind, the emergence and conscious manifestation of the psi bank. How?

The Dreamspell program is the empirical demonstration of fourth-dimensional time. In the fourth dimension time is biology, biology is art, art is time. Galactic biology encompasses living or whole systems in their entirety. Understanding a planet system in its entirety is to experience in a completely aesthetic manner the vivid wholeness of a complex order evolving itself through time. Having relegated our knowing to the third dimension alone, we have cut ourselves off from the fourth, and having done so we have deprived ourselves of the harmonic regularity and synchronic originality that comes of operating within the planetary chronosphere, the fourth dimension. If a thing is not imagined or conceived of as a total element of reality, it will not come to be. Mind participates in its own evolution by such daring acts of the imagination. If the chronosphere is the image of the mental structure and principle that confers the higher-dimensional order to the entire planet as an evolving system, and if the principle of the chronosphere's powers of regeneration is dependent on human mental self-reflectiveness, then the chronosphere introduces the perfect interactive evolutionary mechanism by which humanity can restore order to itself and come to peace with nature.

The planetary chronosphere is the fourth-dimensional envelope that regulates the magnetosphere and radiation belts, the biosphere or ecosystem, and the physical-plane Earth core itself. As such, the chronosphere functions as a moving three-part field structure coordinating the electromagnetic field (magnetosphere and radiation belts, inclusive of the ionosphere); the biopsychic field (biosphere inclusive of the symbiosis of eco-cycles integrating the 'inert' with the 'living corpus'); and the gravitational field (inclusive of the tectonic plate structure, mantles and Earth core).

At present, the belief system of the 12:60 mental field has created an artificial, yet totally illusory, mental shield around the planet. The rigidity of this belief system is all that keeps humanity not only from realizing that the chronosphere exists but also from receiving the enormous benefits of its presence. The 12:60 planetary mental shield is sustained by an artificial feedback loop which is a self-reinforcing system. At the root of this artificial 12:60 system is the belief that time is linear. To accept this belief is to surrender one's free will, for the belief that time is linear consigns the believer into a mental trap that says there is no choice but to go ahead according to the available options, which have all been conditioned by a linear development that can have only one foregone conclusion. In addition to contradicting the facts of the Earth's rotational momentum, spin and orbital circulation, the fatalism of the belief that time is linear generates a mental disease that afflicts all of humanity and the planet without exception.

This mental disease manifests in the order of reality as it is known today, one governed by the principle 'time is money'. The inescapable power of this 12:60 order of reality is referred to as Atlantis Corporation — 'Atlantis' because the very name conjures an amnesiac grandeur and 'corporation' because of the tendency to incorporate everything into a material form that can be exchanged for and/or be valued by money. This is the essence of the 12:60 mental disease, a genuine memory virus that manifests as the artificial planetary mental shield of global materialism.

Yet being artificial the 12:60 mental shield cannot withstand the overpowering effects of the g-force, the natural self-existing 13:20 galactic timing frequency. As the tide of the 13:20 timing frequency washes back in, the 12:60 timing frequency diminishes in power and, like a sandbar occasioned at one moment by perturbations in the geomagnetism affecting the ocean swells, in another moment it is gone again, swallowed by the vast ocean of galactic time. Once it is evident that the 12:60 is merely a rapidly eroding illusion, a lesser sandbar of consciousness, then the election of the collective human will to the higher order of reality will become the easier course.

Since the chronosphere operates at a regular 13:20 frequency, and once humanity is consciously operating on the 13:20 frequency via acceptance of the 13-Moon calendar, then the entire three-part field regulated by the chronosphere will come into resonance with itself. Being in resonance with itself, it will bring forth its own 13:20 mantle of mind — the noosphere — to be activated as the psi bank, the information code that places the third and fourth dimensions in synchronization with each other. The Dreamspell is the set of tools to unlock the psi bank and, in so doing, to evoke the Dreamspell user's own imminent enlightenment. Unlike the artificially generated 12:60 feedback loop, which is like bad air continuously circulated within a closed system, the 13:20 chronospheric feedback loop is galactic in nature and origin. The chronosphere's free operation assures its own illumination.

For humanity, the crux and nexus of this evolutionary shift toward whole illumination — universal transcension — is the need to tend properly to the biosphere. As the biopsychic field, the description of the biosphere is inclusive of its transition into the noosphere. What this means is the conscious interpenetration of the fourth dimension into the third dimension, the evolutionary advancement of the Dreamspell codes into a co-creative unlocking of the memory-generating patterns governing the Earth's own whole systems development. Again, once humanity releases itself from the grip of the artificial 12:60 timing frequency, the flood gates will open.

According to the Dreamspell analysis and critique, humanity is genetically in the driver's seat and has the capacity to bring about the conscious resonance of the three fields of the chronosphere: the electromagnetic, the biopsychic and the gravitational. Through the application of the Dreamspell codes, the human subcorpus of planetary living matter can exert a creative synthesis whereby the electromagnetic field is psychophysically reconstituted through the senses; the biopsychic field is reorganized as the telepathic cosmic order of human society indistinguishable from the living orders of nature; and the gravitational field is brought to a new level of balance through a vibrant correlation and symbiosis of the two third-dimensional geochemical orders SO_2 (silicon dioxide) and CO_2 (carbon dioxide). As far-fetched as this geochemical correlation may seem initially, it is founded on the holon congruence of the different levels and functions of the biosphere considered as an evolving form of time.

The Dreamspell codes of fourth-dimensional time spell out a perfect correspondence between the planet holon (see page 91 and center back, Oracle Board) and the human holon (see page 92 and center back, Journey Board). Governed by the 20 solar frequencies arranged as an icosahedral weave, the planet holon actually consists of three simultaneous movements of different whole icon sets. The simultaneous movement in time of the three weaves constituting the planet holon engenders the chronosphere and its three fields.

a) The set of four weaves running diagonally down to the right from the North pole describes the four chromatic powers of the four clans moved by the overtone fifth. The bi-polar weave of the clan chromatics corresponds to the electromagnetic field of the chronosphere. From the point of view of the fourth dimension, electromagnetism is the function of a second- and fourth-dimensional dynamic. The chromatic clan weave of the planet holon demonstrates the conscious bi-polar linking of the second-dimensional electrical experience of the human sensory realm with the fourth-dimensional magnetic order of time. Currently 'electricity' is hostage to 12:60 interests, and its use is confined to an exploitation of the senses. In the human holon, the bi-polar electromagnetic weave of the chromatics is manifest as the four extremities — the hands and the feet — as well as the four bodily circuits that connect the 20 digits of the hands and feet to the five internal psychophysical centers. Coded within the electromagnetic weave is both the dynamic of the solar-planetary genesis and the movement of time cells and harmonics. In this way the human holon with its third-dimensional root or 'space suit' is in all actuality an already evolved planetary biocomputer.

b) The horizontal cross-weave of the planet holon describes the biopsychic/noospheric field of resonance. While four stitches moving diagonally to the lower right describe the electromagnetic bi-polar field of resonance, the biopsychic consists of five stitches moving horizontally across the planet holon. These five horizontal stitches describe the five Earth Families which code in 73 sequences the 365 days of the Earth's rotation around the sun. The coding of every human being by date of birth according to one of these five Earth Families constitutes the matrix of the biosphere, as well as the capacity of the biosphere to transmute into the noosphere. (See Postlude: Vernadsky's Biomass Constant) The chromatic staggering of the horizontal movement of the five Earth families stabilizes the third-dimensional Earth within the noosphere.

Within the individual human corpus, the biopsychic field is located in the five psychophysical centers of consciousness aligned along the central axis. The resonance of these five centers with each other stabilizes the human holon within the moving body, providing a unified base from which all sentiency may radiate.

To the biocomputer crown of the human corresponds the northern Arctic region of the Earth, governed by the bar Polar Earth family. To the throat center of human speech corresponds the North temperate continental region of the Earth, governed by the one-dot Cardinal Earth Family. To the human heart center of innate knowing correspond the equatorial tropics and central core of the Earth, governed by the two-dot Core Earth family. To the solar plexus intuitive knowing center of the human corresponds the south temperate

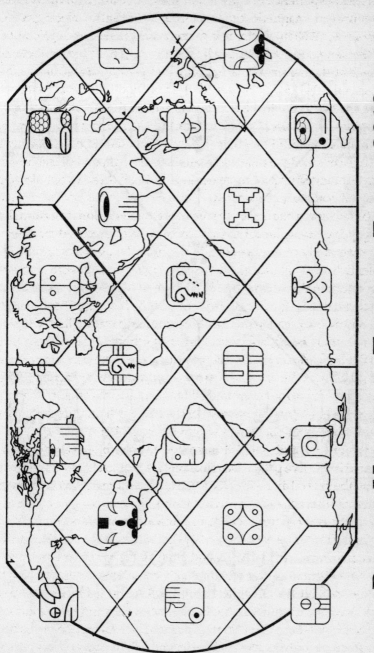

PLANET HOLON — TIMESHIP EARTH 2013

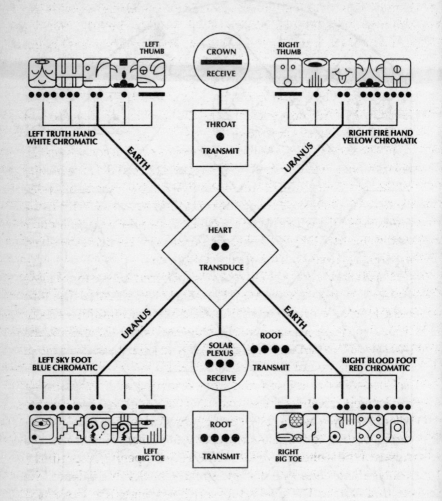

HUMAN HOLON
KNOW YOUR FINGERS AND TOES

oceanic zone of the Earth, governed by the three-dot Signal Earth Family. Finally to the human sexual root center corresponds the southern Antarctic region of the Earth, governed by the four-dot gateway Earth family. In these five sets of human-planetary holon correspondences are constituted the effective means of understanding the deeper substratum of the genetic and psychic changes necessary for transmuting the biosphere into the noosphere, the fulfillment of the biopsychic field as the crowning achievement of Earth's evolving chronosphere.

c) The third level of stitching of the planet holon constitutes the gravitational field of resonance. The gravitational field is stitched by the four color families in motion upward from the South pole, running diagonally opposite the chromatic weave. Gravity is the coherence of the whole system with itself, creating a single unitary whole. Gravity implies coherent balance of elements resolved through a primary binary power of attraction.

This binary power of attraction is provided by the four colors arranged as two sets of attractive and attracting values. The four color families create a gravitational stabilization into two sets of primal antipodal values: red and blue, and white and yellow; the two sets of two values each interactively resolve themselves into a single binary unit of gravitational balance.

The values of the red and blue, initiating and transforming respectively, resolve themselves into a single gravitational value balance, known as the self-existing-lunar value. The tonal values corresponding to the self-existing and the lunar are 4 and 2. The values of the white and yellow, refining and ripening respectively, resolve themselves into a single gravitational value balance, the electromagnetic. The tonal values corresponding to the electro- and magnetic are 3 and 1 respectively. Resolved into two gravitational value balances, the self-existing-lunar and the electromagnetic, the gravitational field generates the other two fields. It is precisely because the electromagnetic value is one of the two composite forces by which gravity is maintained that it can be generated as a field in its own right.

The gravitational order of balance provided by the color families creates an energetic organizational mold for the human holon to enter as it proceeds in its own process of cosmic reabsorption into a simpler yet more expansive sensory and social order. In bringing the gravitational field of the human-planetary holon to a level of conscious resonance, human reality may radically simplify itself to a post-technological synthesis of means, bringing about a corresponding expansion of sensory programs and mental awareness.

In the context of the Dreamspell the four-color weave of the gravitational field of resonance is also referred to as the four root races. Because each time cell consists of one member each of the four root races, the working order of time demonstrates the cooperative order of social reality. Organized as the four root races, the movements of the human social order may participate in maintaining the gravitational order of the Earth while participating in an ever-changing hierarchy of temporal functions and realities. In this way, the human social order will synthesize itself more and more with the total order of the biosphere, as the biosphere itself transmutes into the noosphere.

The effective method for bringing about this gravitational synthesis of social and geochemical order is to be found in the harmonization of the two orders of biospheric reality presented by the third-dimensional SO_2 and CO_2 molecular programs. The SO_2 silicon dioxide order of reality represents the 'inert' corpus of the Earth's biosphere, and the key underlying matrix of Earth's dense physical core. CO_2, the carbon dioxide cycle, is the base of the program sustaining the corpus of living matter, or biomass, from the photosynthesis of plants to the respiration of the human organism.

As SO_2, the quartz crystal represents a maximally radial simplification of form with a maximum increase of transduction capacity — the power to change one state of energy into another.

As the key genetic component of the CO_2 cycle, the human represents a maximally radial complexification of form with a maximum increase in sentiency — the power to absorb new feeling states in full self-reflective absorbency. Both crystal and human are complete resonators of the radial matrix. A future, yet immediately realizable, means for accelerating the evolution of the biosphere into the noosphere is to be found in this simple symbiotic translation: the unfathomed ranges of human sentiency applied by mental means to crystal transduction. In this way the advent of the noosphere is prepared, the evolution of the biosphere into expanded states of transductive sentiency opening to untold possibilities of sentient transduction. One chronosphere, one planet, one interdependent spectrum of evolutionary possibilities: the realization of the harmonic convergence of the SO_2 and CO_2 cycles will open vistas to the creation of the planet art spore.

Operating as the internalization of the three fields of resonance, and allowing the socially reorganizing capacity of the Dreamspell codes to impact on their own perceptions, humans will liberate untold amounts of psychic energy now long pent up within the artificial 12:60 mental shield. The release of these energies, creatively moderated by the planetary service wavespell of the 13-Moon Calendar, will bring about the telepathic reorganization of human society.

But first humanity must use the new calendar to come to terms with its own belief in money as a value. The 13-moon restructuring of this belief will result in planetary programs to equalize the current status of wealth. With the reordering of concepts of wealth mandated by the new calendar, existing political forms will also be streamlined and used to create an orderly transition out of the 12:60 institutional realm and back into nature. This return to the natural order will be opened up first of all by a concerted effort to clean up and restore the environment, followed by realization of the laws unifying the human mental experience with the larger timing frequency governing nature, the 13:20.

The sum of these early efforts at self-reorganization according to the new calendar and re-entry into the proper timing frequency will establish humanity in an accelerated evolutionary trajectory. Understanding at last the nature of time, living at last in time with nature, humanity will know time as advancement into sensory mental realms of experience only enhanced by the telepathic capacity to know as one and to penetrate and enter whatever needs to be known. Since time is biology, and biology is art, in this tuning of the human into its own natural timing frequency lies the capacity for the whole system Earth to attain its evolutionary resolution as a planetary art spore. More than this I cannot say, for my vision is only my vision. It is for the intelligence of the entire collective corpus humanity to make the choice it has to make.

As I stated at the outset, science is an evolutionary phenomenon.

When the programs by which we live are no longer anything more than orders of self-maintenance, the laws by which our own evolution and self-reflection are governed are to be discovered or even invented anew. Having presented here the principles, mathematical proofs and empirical demonstrations of time as the fourth dimension, the purpose of this treatise has been fulfilled.

Embodied in the Dreamspell kit are possibilities of chronomancy not touched upon in this book. The reverse sides of the Oracle and Journey Boards contain the minimal demonstration necessary to convey the operating mechanisms of the chronosphere, and the rudiments of the new science of chronomancy. This aside, if one follows carefully what is written herein, and is possessed by no inhibitions to learning anew, treasures long concealed by Earth and the unconscious mind will show themselves in supernatural clarity and logic.

Concluded in honor of the Arcturian Watch
Kin 164 Yellow Galactic Seed,
Overtone Moon, Day 14
Blue Cosmic Storm Year

Part IV

APPENDICES

Practicing the Universal Equality of Awareness

The fundamental technique for cultivating the state of nowness is referred to as 'practicing the universal equality of awareness'. This is the only way to maintain genuine freshness of mind. Without this freshness of mind, the conditionings of the 12:60 timing frequency will continue to occlude clear seeing and the capacity for extended sensory vision or fourth-dimensional insight. In these two capacities of mind, clear seeing and extended sensory vision, are the two goals of practicing the universal equality of awareness.

This practice is called universal because it can be undertaken by any human, and its object of experience is the universal nature of mind which is nothing more than the uncategorized equality of all phenomena and experiences with each other. The experience of universal equality is maintained by an awareness that is actually constant or constantly available in the moment by bringing your mind back to it. Practice of the universal equality of awareness brings about a mind that is without judgement yet discriminating, calm yet vigilant, and receptive to synchronic nuances of sensory mental input — extended sensory vision, which is the root of telepathic fourth-dimensional knowing and experience. All of these qualities of mind are in the now, and free of third-dimensional conceptual clinging.

To practice universal equality of awareness, first understand the nature of mind, then the nature of mind as it has been conditioned by the 12:60 timing frequency.

The nature of mind is unobstructed clarity contaminated by neither content nor goal; its energetic capacity is to appreciate and spontaneously formulate sensory input into catalytic imagery capable of being communicated and/or translated into bodily movement or action. If the mind remains fresh and open, bodily movement and action remain spontaneous and free. Self-esteem is the spiritual root of the body moving in time. Without self-esteem there is no patience to watch the mind; without watching and knowing the mind, the body will not be able to move freely in time.

Immersed in and conditioned by the 12:60 timing frequency, the mind loses its inherent freshness; its spontaneity is drastically reduced, becoming constantly ego-specific in its orientation, goal-oriented in its referencing, and clock-dependent in its governance. Not knowing any other way, these attributes of mind become second nature, collectively creating the 12:60 mental field called materialism. Materialism is mental addiction to a belief in the exclusive power of third-dimensional physical plane reality. The root of materialism as a state of mind is conditioned by the regimen of the seven-day week (see below: 'Concerning the Atlantis Corporation').

Even though 52 weeks follow in perfect regularity, the irregular reckoning of the 12-month calendar is not in accord with the seven-day week. For this reason, the days of the week and the days of the month are continuously different and random, month after month, year after year. This conditions the 12:60 mind to egoic shortsightedness on behalf of the attainment of its own survival goals, and amnesia about all else.

The coherent capacity of the mind to entrain a cyclic comprehension of no more than a generic week is further reinforced by money, which is rewarded for the time one has given to a job during five days of the week. In this way the week becomes the measure of time allotted to 'earn one's bread', while the weekend becomes the primary and all-consuming goal or escape-valve. The shut-down this creates to the original unobstructed condition of mind is profound; but when the clock is thrown in as the instrument for regulating one's bodily momentum, then the situation of the 12:60 timing frequency becomes totally unnatural and unhealthy.

The inherent problem of the clock is the profound lack of trust it engenders in the body's own inherent timing frequency. The arbitrary division of the day — one kin — into 24 hours, each hour into 60 minutes, each minute into 60 seconds, and each second, by means of cesium atomic clocks, reducible to infinitesimal portions of itself, all of this factored into an endless, random, unpatterned relationship of months to days of the week, results in a mental situation of chaotic simultaneity and entropic solutionlessness.

Even humans who practice some form of meditation, mental awareness training, or prayer and spiritual service inevitably succumb to the grinding ceaselessness of the clock-fueled state of consciousness known as 12:60 materialism. It is for this reason that the practice of universal awareness of equality becomes mandatory in order to release oneself from the conditions of the 12:60 and to entrain the mind in the 13:20 frequency.

The first step is to cultivate clear seeing. Since mind is originally unobstructed clarity of awareness, and since, in truth, the equality of this awareness never ceases, no matter how much 12:60 conceptualization is generated as second-nature reality, one has only to understand this: no matter what its content, any thought or conceptualization experienced by the mind is self-generated and devoid of any real substance, a mere electroneural flash and nothing more.

By sitting still and holding the spine erect yet relaxed, watch the flow of thoughts. By watching the flow of thoughts one can see that in actuality no thought is more or less important than any other; it is only different ego attachments that make them seem so. Seeing the current of thoughts in this way one can experience the universal equality of awareness as the flow of thoughts undifferentiated by egoic evaluation. By doing this for a few moments at a time, and extending it as one becomes more familiar with the practice, one can come to distinguish that there is actually 'space' between thoughts. This space between thoughts is the original unobstructed nature of mind. Through further practice one can extend oneself for longer periods into this non-conceptualized space. To experience this space is to taste the essence of nowness. In the space of now there is no history, no 12:60, no ego, no beginning and no end. Because one learns to see without concepts, cultivating this space is called cultivating clear seeing.

Within the space of nowness, time continuously arises. Awareness of the time within the non-conceptual space is referred to as panoramic awareness. Panoramic awareness is the universal equality of mind attentive to the total experience of the body and mind as a unified movement in time. Sitting still in panoramic awareness, and entering freely without goal into the qualities of sensory experience which spontaneously occur, is called cultivating extended sensory vision. It is through cultivating extended sensory vision that genuine insight may arise.

This insight, occurring in the space of nowness between and even within thoughts, is referred to as synchronic insight, for it is a result not of a belabored, conditioned process of 12:60 mental rationalization, but of a simultaneous fusion of sensory-psychic input given comprehension through time. Growing out of a familiarity with extended sensory vision, synchronic insight is the basis of the realization of divinatory intelligence, the direct form of knowing necessary for the practice of chronomancy. All divination is direct application of intelligence.

Intelligence is the other attribute of mind which balances awareness. Both awareness and intelligence are factors of resonance permeating all constructs of reality. While awareness, clear seeing and the cultivation of synchronic insight is rooted in mental attentiveness to sensory input (including its own), intelligence refers to the resonant strata of time which order the synchronic manifestation of phenomena.

In nature the resonant strata of time are the schedule of frequencies by which coherence is maintained in the phenomenal world, the world perceptible to the senses. Within the mind, resonant strata of time refers to the schedule of frequencies by which psychic coherence is maintained, and the different orders of psychic information are made available, inclusive of their means of communication, i.e. telepathy. Relieved of the burdens of having to maintain the artificial mental order of the 12:60 consciousness, the mind releases itself easily into its own intelligence. Knowing is innate. Experience transcends further instruction.

Finally, universal equality of awareness is maintained through attention to breath. Whether while sitting with spine erect or at any time of the waking life, if the distraction of 12:60 mental rationalizations becomes overwhelming, it is easy to wake up, take note and return to the breath. In other words, let the complex conceptualization be released with the exhalation, and with the new inhalation let there be clear mind of nowness. Since the respiration of the human corpus represents the other end of the CO_2 cycle generated by plant photosynthesis, the human intelligence brought consciously to bear on the breath results in a restoration of universal equality of awareness within the CO_2 cycle itself. In this way, practiced and understood by growing numbers of the human corpus, universal equality of awareness becomes the basis of a galactic culture. Galactic culture is culture free of all historical, culturally limiting chauvinisms, opening instead to the life of universal equality of all kin.

Universal Transcension

When the days of the 52 weeks are regulated within the 13 perfect moons, then the practice of universal awareness may become normalized. For the first time in its history, the individual and collective human enter the dimension of time purely through mind. Clear seeing and synchronic insight become the universal norm of human awareness. The planetary subcorpus human, maturing in synchronic unison, gives rise to the potential of universal transcension. Universal transcension is the capacity of the subcorpus human to elevate itself simultaneously as a whole organism beyond any confusion and doubt into a synchronic experience beyond any limitation whatsoever.

Synchronic insight, the direct form of knowing through time, faster than the speed of light, puts universal awareness at g-force zero. G-force is the fifth force experienced as the strata of time informing the quality of nowness. Zero refers to the point of total egoic detachment which allows the experience of clear seeing. At g-force zero there is a cancellation of all debts and the arising of the sentiment of universal forgiveness, which is the same as love. The power of g-force zero easily translates into an active capacity capable of transmuting values as they have stratified into institutionalized 12:60 social norms.

In full-blown 12:60 materialism, the core of stratified social norms is embedded within a complex of behavioral models controlled by a political-economic structure in which governmental budgetary allocations for public services are balanced by corporate venues of private services and merchandise, the whole of it held together by the continuous injection and circulation of surplus money.

The complex of behavioral models within this ungainly, artificial 12:60 institutional structure focuses on the temporal sequence of a week, with payments due on a monthly basis, supplemented by the concept of an annual vacation. This entire complex operates on a 12:60 timing frequency where there is no probability factor in time regarding the relationship of weeks to months resulting in a bewildering endlessness of process, while the money-clock prorates the value of everything, causing government institutions to multiply, budget deficits to increase, and corporations to scramble for the endless production of novelty.

All the while, the impact of the frenzied human 12:60 activity destroys its natural environment, yet offers no vision for a possible human existence other than the 12:60 way of life. All of this artificial and uncontrollable momentum of human activity is due to a single mental error: the belief that time is what is measured by a clock, or — even more currently — that time is merely a digital read-out. There is no inherent purpose or end to the 12:60 measurement of time which is ultimately a merciless subjugation of the human will to an arbitrary mental order institutionalized as religion, corporate structures and government.

Since all current budgets worldwide, both government and corporate, are calculated and hopelessly bound according to the 12-month calendar, the transition of this 12:60-regulated complex to the 13-moon calendar can be done in only one way: zero budget.

Zero budget is the translation of g-force zero into the political realm of human affairs. The institutions of government and money are both the materialized outgrowth of a mental concept. Like any thought, the concepts 'money' and 'government' are ultimately an illusion. Governments exist as an outgrowth of the belief that humans are not intelligent, good or strong enough of and among themselves to take care of themselves. The very notion of government is ultimately a disempowering one that negates the potential of genuine autonomy. Money exists as an outgrowth of a belief that time can be quantified and made equivalent to an arbitrary set of values translatable as power over material and psychic reality, which is time.

Zero budget erases the time and energy spent on recovering debts resulting from fictional and arbitrary systems of the human mind, and turns this time and energy into the question: how does one translate money back into time? Take the power out of money, separate money from the clock. Abolish interest banking and all arbitrary hierarchies of wage and profit. Money now becomes the available surplus to be disbursed with the intention of stabilizing the vast inequalities of wealth now existing among humans, and to transform the planetary wastelands devastated by industrialization into galactic parks.

Zero budget means all debts forgiven, everything is at a new beginning. Establish new priorities according to the new time, priorities which promote development of procedures for ever more autonomous action in ever more decentralized bioregions. Since in the new time all the days, weeks and months are regular and even, priorities and goals can be established so that zero budget can be a monthly possibility. This means that income is matched by expenditures, and all disbursements are final. The last disbursements of money are to be allocated so that the recipients use it to establish autonomy. As the money system is devalued, so will the government institutional orders return themselves into decentralized service functions overseeing the process of universal education into the new time, and the translation of the new time into forms of environmental restoration and equality of human rights promoting abundance, health and unlimited sensory expansion.

Since private property, rent and so forth are all fictions of the 12:60, these institutions will fall away. Money will no longer be used as an instrument of power and the privatization of time into space or real estate. In the new time, moving in synchronic unison to the overtone fifth, human values will shift from money as individualized expressions of power to the accumulation of kin credits through the sponsoring of and participation in planetary potlatches: synchronic time-sharing events in which all goods and services are equally valuable and exchangeable. In this way, over a period of a few years, operating according to the rich symphony of time values, humans will experience an equality undreamed of in the age of democracy, and turning in synchronic unison to the measure of the overtone fifth, they will be enfolded into the invisible hierarchy of time in fulfillment of the needs of universal transcension.

Concerning the Atlantis Corporation

'Atlantis Corporation' is referred to as a mental disease which takes the form of an amnesiac compulsion to materially incorporate all human needs and services into functions of a privately controlled value system called 'money'. In this system money represents power over time; however, the production and circulation of money are strictly controlled, and in order to obtain any of the money, which is the only recognized instrument of power and exchange, one must sell one's time to an 'employer' in exchange for it. This system has been aptly called 'wage slavery'. Where did it begin? Why does it continue? Why do humans seem powerless in the face of the Atlantis Corporation?

The Atlantis Corporation has its roots in the Babylonian ghost religion of twelve. It is referred to as a ghost religion because it is a fraudulent imitation of true spirituality, a false order of reality born of a fundamental abuse of power and need to subjugate free will, which are the same thing. The roots of this perversion reached beyond Babylon to evoke a primal Atlantis in which power was stratified into loss of equality, and the resulting abuse destroyed the very civilization which it created.

The Babylonian loss of equality placed men over women, and reduced the 13 annual moons, the power of time, into a calendar of 12, the power of space. Henceforth, time was to be the pawn of imperial space, enslaved as power units to be known as money. Thus was born the first corporate male hierarchy, a ghost culture of the power of 12 held by men in robes. Transmitted as a corporate hierarchical structure holding power over time and history, according to the corporate rules of the game, the only way to negotiate further power was by the use of the inverted power symbol, money. To sustain itself, this male hierarchical ghost culture of the power of 12 instituted taxation and promoted the technology of war to justify its need to collect money and expand its power base.

From Babylonia the power of 12 spread throughout the Mideast, to India and China to the East, and the Mediterranean basin to the West. To a greater or lesser degree, the Babylonian power standard of 12 was adopted throughout the civilized world of the Eurasian landmass. As a complex number, 12 represents the power of a self-perpetuating stasis. All of civilization as it has evolved to the present time is an expression of the static power of 12.

To the 12-part division of the year, derived from a 12-part division of the circle as the power of space, the Babylonian-Atlantean ghost time religion also evoked the power of seven — hence 7-day week, 12-month year. The purpose of the 7-day week was to create a yoke in which to contain human energy in units small and easy enough to translate into monetary equivalents. In this way, human life became portioned out in accountant's dribbles, the horizons of survival became lowered to the threshold of daily bread, and the priests and their imperial orders were able to gain greater and greater control over third-dimensional existence.

The corporate structure of the Babylonian priesthood only grew in customs and complexity, finally to be transmitted to the decaying imperial power structure of ancient Rome. The true inheritor of the corporate Babylonian power structure was the Christian Church. Like the original ghost religion of Babylon, based on the power of 12 covering up the 13th moon, the power structure of the Christian Church was used to cover up Jesus, who was a true emanation of the universal light of the power of Thirteen. In AD 321, Emperor Constantine consolidated the Roman imperial order with the Christian Church, and adopted the 7-day week to the 12-month calendar. The Babylonian ghost culture was now grafted on to the Christian Church.

By the 13th century AD, the success of the ghost splinter of the Neo-Babylonian Christian Church of Rome was consolidated. The virus of the Atlantis Corporation was now totally locked up within the secret chambers of the Vatican. At the heart of this power consolidation was complete power over time and history: the Julian calendar, inherited from the Romans, who inherited it from the Babylonians. The 7-day week and the 12-month year now owned by the Church in the form of the Julian calendar was to be converted into a complete system for translating time and property into money, where money in and of itself was to be a very strictly controlled instrument of power. In this way, since money is only an abstraction of stolen time, the creator of intoxicatingly fictional values, the money system evolved as the chief instrument furthering the creation of a worldwide ghost culture, the Planetary Atlantis Corporation.

With power over time the Church zealously watched over and financed the European conquest of the world to make sure it maintained its power over history as well. In 1583 following the securing of its dominion over the planet, the reformed 7-day week, twelve-month Gregorian calendar was instituted by the Vatican, essentially sealing the planet within the Babylonian ghost religion of the Atlantis Corporation. With the concurrent mechanization of the clock was born the disease of global materialism. Henceforth, all understanding of time would stop at the docile and unconscious acceptance of the 12-month Gregorian calendar, only to be calculated in monetary terms according to the arbitrary divisions of clock-time. In AD 1992, to affirm its control over time and history, the Church, issuing its first catechism since 1555, declared mediumship to be a sin whose purpose is to gain personal power over time and history. Holding the calendar of 12, the Church keeps the planet within the grip of its version of time and history.

The Protestant Reformation against the power of the Roman Church only resulted in the creation of protestant ghost splinters of the larger Babylonian-Roman ghost splinter. While the Roman Church consolidated the neo-Babylonian Gregorian calendar of 12, the ghost splinters of protestantism created a 'secular' base for the mechanization of time and the conversion of money into the ultimate determining and controlling human value.

The combination of the two factors — the control of the planet by the calendar of 12 and the mechanization of the 60-minute hour — had the immediate effect of accelerating the DNA of the human species. Since 1583, a 400-year population explosion has occurred, irrevocably altering the traditional social bases of human society. At the same time, under the auspices of the explosion of the perfection of the artificial and arbitrary 12:60 timing frequency, human engineering and industrial machinery have impacted exponentially on the geological processes of the global ecosystem, hastening the imminent transition of the biosphere into the noosphere. As acceleration increases, probability of change from within the 12:60 system reduces to zero. The absolute zero point of 12:60 time can only result in the entrainment back into the natural galactic timing frequency of 13:20. This event occurs within the climax of the spiralling sickness of the Atlantis Corporation.

Though spawned by the Catholic Church, by AD 1754, the Atlantis Corporation had sprouted its own gorgon-headed monster: the industrial-democratic revolutionary wave. Backed by an elite of bankers, by the 19th century this revolutionary wave become the dominant world force. Though the Church had lost influence as its royal patronage and power base shrank, it still held the trump card of the power over time and history, the Gregorian Calendar. When Italy became democratic, the Church was temporarily orphaned. But in 1928 the Fascist government of Italy recognized the Vatican as a political entity. Since that time the Pope and the Vatican have continued to exert major influence world-wide. Why?

Not only does the Vatican hold the calendar which runs the planet, but it allows unrestricted import and export of money from its banks which otherwise operate under a veil of secrecy. 12:60 time, 12:60 money: why does the Vatican still hold all this power? Because it is still the Babylonian stronghold of the ghost culture of Atlantis. This ghost culture is also known as the Mafia, the international consortium of cartels who assure the free circulation of money, guns and drugs. Break the power of 12 by the return of the 13 moons, and the Babylonian power of ghost Atlantis will dissolve.

The relation between the current world calendar and the banking system supported by it must be objectively understood. By placing everyone within the unceasingly random pace of the 12-month calendar, a fateful uncertainty of time is created in which the best hope against a destiny of drudgery is a winning lottery ticket. This shows that the 12-month calendar is not about time but control. The 13-moon calendar is not random but regular; every week of every month is the same every year. Certainty replaces doubt. At the same time, because the 13-moon calendar is moved by the 260-kin galactic spin, the effect is the creation of a timing frequency in which two highly regular timing devices combine to create a probability spectrum of 18,980 self-regulating permutations. In other words no two kin/days are the same in a 52-year cycle.

While the 12-month calendar is both random and improbable with a resultant sense of doom or hopelessness, the 13-moon calendar is regular but, engaged with the galactic spin, is capable of sustaining a very high degree of spontaneous novelty or innovation. This will have the effect of promoting an expanded sense of individual free will self-regulation in an ever greater turning of creative events of synchronic unison. This free-will 13:20 entrainment will depose in a twinkling the impostors of the ghost culture of the Atlantis Corporation, while assuring the human race its entry into the dimension of time.

Formula of the Overtone Fifth: Transition to the Noosphere

Entering fully into the dimension of time means that humanity is finally completing itself. Space is easy to conquer, time is impossible. But if one releases oneself into time, then all things are possible. Unified in time, the human race will become self-regulated by time. Objectified as the fourth-dimensional chronosphere, time is the self-regulating mechanism of the planet. To set the chronosphere in motion according to the galactic 13:20 timing frequency is the meaning and purpose of the transition of the biosphere to the noosphere.

The biosphere is constituted of the inert and the organic, represented by the SO_2 and the CO_2 molecular orders respectively. The SO_2 standard is the quartz crystal which exemplifies the constancy of form necessary for maximum transduction. Unobstructed clarity and purity of form facilitate direct unmediated crystal transductions of electricity from the fourth to the second dimensions, and from kinetic to electric states within the second dimension. The standard for the CO_2 cycle is the human organism whose peak performance channels through multiple sensory outlets the overtone cyclic fluidity required for maximum sentiency. 'Cyclic fluidity' refers to the harmony of the different sense ratios processing input synchronically. Synchronic fusion occurs when the input of the sense ratios self-harmonizes through the production of states of enhanced sensitivity. The entrainment of the SO_2 and the CO_2 cycles occurs through conscious intention of enhanced sensitivity transduced through a crystal, and in phase with the cycles of the overtone fifth.

Synchronically aligned through conscious entrainment of the overtone fifth, the biospheric polarities of the SO_2 and CO_2 molecular frequencies experience a resonant fusion. The overtone fifth SO_2-CO_2 fusion generates a third non-molecular term or agent, the noosphere. The chief characteristic of the noosphere is a transductive sentiency. In transductive sentiency, radial, multidimensional transformations of energy and information at a conscious whole systems level become the self-regulating norm. The transductive sentiency of the noosphere facilitates channels of direct knowing and communication from within the noosphere's operating mechanism, the planet chronosphere. What transpires within the daily spin of the planet chronosphere imprints the psi bank in whole fractal sequences. As the resonant collective memory storage facility, the psi bank releases stored whole fractal sequences to the chronosphere of the individual and/or collective human.

As the daily operating mechanism of the noosphere, the chronosphere is the movement in time of the three fields of the planet holon: the gravitational (Four Root Races), the electromagnetic (the Four Clans) and the biopsychic (the Five Earth Families). The three fields of the planet holon are reciprocally held together by the icosahedral matrix of the holon itself. The icosahedral matrix is pulsed in tonal wave sequences of 13 kin each, riveting the planet holon to the solar-galactic ratios of the galactic spin. The interaction of the three fields with the icosahedral weave pulsed by the series of 13-kin wavespells generates the psi bank, the resonant information 'storage facility' of the chronosphere.

Within the planet holon, and turning in time with the planet chronosphere, is the human holon and its individual chronosphere. The 20-digit human holon is digitalized by the power of the overtone fifth to the icosahedral weave of the planet holon. The medium of exchange between the planet holon and the human holon is the human chronosphere.

Turning in time to the planet chronosphere, the human chronosphere is the registration of the human holon moving in time with the body. The composite of the body moving in time with the holon, and the holon turning within its chronosphere, recapitulates within the individual human holon the self-regulating noospheric fractal of the planet within the planet holon. In this way telepathy may be established between human and human, and human and other elements of the living corpus (CO_2), geomancy between human and Earth (SO_2), and chronomancy between human and time (SO_2-CO_2 fusion). Operating in this way, and in accord with the overtone fifth, the human in time with itself becomes its own expression of health.

The chromatic overtone fifth is the all-inclusive binding principle bringing about the transition of the biosphere into the noosphere, the fusion of the SO_2 and CO_2 cycles, and the human into full resonance with the planet holon. The chromatic overtone fifth is keyed to the biopsychic field of resonance (Five Earth Families, the five horizontal bands of the planet holon weave), pulsed according to the power of the five-unit chromatic code, or overtone fifth. The overtone fifth moves in the following manner: four dot—bar—one dot—two dot—three dot. When one overtone chromatic fifth is completed by the three-dot frequency, a new chromatic begins again on the four dot.

This formula of the overtone fifth may be synchronically mapped on the planet and human holons respectively as the movement that begins at the South Polar zone (planet), root center (human); then jumps to the North Polar zone (planet), crown center (human); then moves downward through the North continental zone (planet), throat center (human); to the Core-Equatorial zone (planet), heart center (human); completing itself in the South Oceanic zone (planet), solar plexus center (human). The process then repeats with the next four-dot frequency.

In terms of the five Earth families (the biopsychic weave of the planet holon), the code of the overtone fifth proceeds in the following manner: Gateway family (four dot), Polar family (bar), Cardinal family (one dot), Core Family (two dot) and Signal Family (three dot). This program in time codes the sequence of the 365 kin of the Earth's solar orbit in a set of 73 perfect fifths of five kin or five days each ($73 \times 5 = 365$). Pulsed by the 13 tones in its vortical sequences of 20 wavespells each, the overtone fifth movement pattern sets the planet holon in motion, creating the chronosphere and generating the psi bank. Moved by the overtone fifth within the vortical pulsations of the galactic spin, the biopsychic weave is responsible for the galactic signatures which imprint each day (kin) and which provide each human with his/her planetary kin identification through day (kin) of birth. Once the human is turning within the correct timing frequency — 13:20 — then a new definition of the ideal human may arise: a self-regulating biopsychic chronosphere, the autonomous human consciously turning in time with the noosphere.

Because of the sequence of overtone fifths, the first kin of the solar year is always a Gateway four-dot kin, while green day — the day out of time — is always a Signal three-dot kin. This sequence of 73 overtone fifths weaves the 13 perfect moons of 28 days each, the third-dimensional time template to the fourth-dimensional template of the 260-kin galactic spin. The relationship of 73 overtone chromatics per solar orbit to the 52 weeks (plus one kin) of the 13-moon calendar is the inverse of the relationship of 73 galactic spins to the perfect solar-galactic cycle of 52 years. The formula for the overtone fifth is expressed in the following way:

52 fifths	= 260 kin	= 1 Galactic Spin
73 fifths	= 52 weeks (+1 kin)	= 1 Solar Orbit
52 solar orbits	= 73 galactic spins	= 1 Solar-Galactic cycle
	ratio: 5:7 :: 7:5	

While the 52 weeks taken in bundles of four create the 13 moons, the set of 73 overtone fifths paces and governs the orbit of the planet around the sun. As the basis of the experience of synchronic unison, turning in time to the overtone fifth, which gives rise to universal transcension, the set of overtone fifths is to be understood in the following way:

18 sets of four fifths each (20 kin) = 72 fifths

72 fifths = 360 kin, one planetary orbit less one fifth

$72 = (1/2 \ 144$, fractal of third-to-fourth interdimensional transmutation into light)

360 kin = 72 x 5 (18 x 20) = one Tun = one solar-terrestrial synchronic registration

360 kin/one Tun + 4 kin (one Harmonic) = 364 kin =

91 (x 4) Harmonics = 364 kin =

13 Moons (x 28) = 52 (x 7) weeks =

360 + (4+1 (green day)) = 365 = 72 fifths plus one

(the perfect fifth) = 73 fifths

73 fifths = one solar orbit of Timeship Earth

As long as one remembers that the sequence of overtone fifths is always coded according to the Gateway family, which always codes the first day of the first of the 13 moons, then one can pick up and follow the pattern of the overtone fifths. When, through the practice of universal equality of awareness, one follows the chromatic sequence of the overtone fifth both in oneself, a bodily center per day kin, and through the body moving to the whole kin sequence of the galactic spin, this is called generating the biopsychic chromatic. The result of practicing the biopsychic chromatic induces the telepathic resonance of the body with itself, with other members of the biosphere, with the Earth, and with the psi bank registrations of the chronosphere.

Because the movement of the overtone chromatic goes from the root to the crown, the South to North polar zones of the planet, the overtone chromatic weaves the human and planet holons together and links two different Chromatic Clan sequences, assuring continuous movement in time. The movement of the overtone fifth chromatic is also tracked on the wavespell as the five sets of overtone pulsars.

Through the exposition and demonstration of the principle of the chromatic overtone fifth, 73 per solar orbit of planet system Earth, and in coordination with all of the other cyclic strata of time — harmonics, wavespells, castles, spins, 13 moons and the larger cycles inclusive of and leading beyond the 52-year fractal, the human organism in conscious reciprocity with itself and the other elements of the ecosphere brings about the manifestation of the noosphere. The 73 annual overtone fifths provide the noosphere articulation as the chronosphere. As the movement in time of the evolved noospheric planet system, the chronosphere establishes the full range of biopsychic potential for the human moving into full exploration of the fourth dimension.

This evolutionary movement is both a natural occurrence and a result of human free will. It is a natural occurrence because Earth already moves through its progression of overtone fifths, and its natural timing frequency of 13:20 is already established, accounting for the innate health of virtually all species of the biosphere except the human. Yet the human, lacking health and appropriate timing vitality, affects the health of all the other species. Self-regulated according to the proper timing frequencies and the majestic regularity of the overtone fifth, as humankind regains its health, the living corpus of the biosphere will correct itself. Deep understanding and practice of the overtone fifth in conjunction with the chronomantic science of the pulsars will lead to an elimination of disease and the creation of a spectacular level of creative order within the ranks of human society regenerated in its own time.

The transition of the biosphere into the noosphere, and the establishment of the 13:20 timing frequency among all humans was initiated by the free will option known as the 144 days of Harmonic Convergence. This refers to the first 144 days of the harmonic spin that began on Red Magnetic Dragon, Kin 1, Gregorian date, March 5, 1993, and concluded Kin 144, Yellow Magnetic Seed, July 26, 1993. The opportunity afforded to growing numbers of humanity in consciously following these 144 days, kin after kin, culminating in the commencement of the next 13-moon solar cycle, is without precedent. The consciously activated 144 days of Harmonic Convergence constituted the creation of a galactic free zone in time. The accomplishment of the replacement of the Gregorian calendar by the Calendar of the 13 Moons by the completion of these 144 days, Kin 144, would inaugurate Earth as a galactic entity whose noosphere could now be guaranteed to flower. When the new time has arrived on Earth, the new genesis will be in full flower. Humanity's evolution will be secured. Planet Earth will have come of age.

The Five Time Cell/Castle Action Commands:

Red Time Cell One, Input:
Inform turning, initiate seed birth

White Time Cell Two, Store:
Remember crossing, refine warrior death

Blue Time Cell Three, Process:
Formulate burning, transform star magic

Yellow Time Cell Four, Output:
Express giving, ripen sun intelligence

Green Time Cell Five, Matrix:
Self-regulate enchantment, synchronize human free will

Klatu Barada Nikto — The Galactic Federation Comes in Peace!

Postlude

VERNADSKY'S BIOMASS CONSTANT — AN EQUATION IN TIME

No whole systems thinking on the matter of the biosphere has been as comprehensive as that of Vladimir Vernadsky (1863-1944). Not only was his thinking comprehensive, but it was impeccably scientific, elegantly simple and synthesizing. Though published in 1926, Vernadsky's *Biosphere* presents a description of the planetary whole system that is logically so consistent and far-reaching in its implications that it must stand among the greatest contributions to human knowledge.

At its core, Vernadsky's description of the biosphere may be stated as a matter of a few logical premises. The inescapable conclusion to these logical premises describing the biosphere points to the imminent transition of the biosphere into the noosphere and the advent of what Vernadsky calls the psychozoic era.

At the conclusion to his lifetime studies on the geochemical dynamic of the biosphere, Vernadsky's description of the biosphere as the function of a set of scientific laws was lacking in two points: 1) a lack of the precise geometries of time by which to understand the governance of the laws of the biosphere with regard to evolutionary mutations, inclusive of the transition to the noosphere, and 2) lacking these geometries of time, the precise conditions and results of the transition of the biosphere into the noosphere also remained vague.

As I have demonstrated in this book, the laws and mathematics of the geometry of time which govern the evolutionary phases of the whole planet system are purely fourth-dimensional in nature and as such are totally apart from the mathematics and geometries of space or the third dimension. Established by the Maya as the mathematics of solar-galactic timing frequencies, the geometry of time as the fourth dimension is only just now, as a result of this treatise, capable of being understood within a whole planet systems frame of reference. As a result, we have an immediate application of this fourth-dimensional knowledge to the current geological opportunity, the biospheric-noospheric transition.

In homage to the great pioneer Vladimir Vernadsky, I will now demonstrate the conclusion to the two unresolved points of his research through an application of the laws and geometries of fourth-dimensional time. Lacking any such accurate understanding of the unique existence of these laws and geometries, any view of the Earth as a whole system will be incomplete.

The premises of the Vernadsky biospheric equation are as follows.

1. The biosphere is the dynamic envelope of planet Earth for the transformation of cosmic energy (solar, galactic radiation).

2. The effect of the biospheric transformations of energy results in a complex of ongoing geochemical transformations.

3. The constitution of the biosphere is of both inert and living matter. The relationship between the inert and living in turn constitutes the realm of geochemistry.

4. Throughout all geological ages the chemical effects of living matter on its surroundings have not changed, so that the chemical composition of the crust and of the living matter are the same today as they have always been.

5. The living matter of the biosphere is a single corpus, governed by a common genetic code.

6. The single corpus of the biomass is a constant: "The total mass of living matter has never differed considerably from its present value."

7. Evolutionary sequences are highly varied for different species, ocean and land, but the sum evolutionary interactions may be considered as functions of the biogenic migration of atoms in the shifting geochemical give-and-take of the inert and living corpus.

8. "The evolution of different forms of life throughout the geological time increases the biogenic migration of elements in the biosphere."

9. "The evolution of species, in tending towards the creation of new forms of life, must always move in the direction of increasing biogenic migration of atoms in the biosphere."

10. The course of the processes of evolution must proceed in the direction of increasing consciousness and thought, and of forms of life having greater and greater influence on their surroundings.

11. The question: "How can processes which seem purely physical be affected by consciousness?" asked by Vernadsky in conclusion to *Biosphere*, is answered: "The correct understanding of time demonstrates how what seem to be purely physical processes may be affected by consciousness, for time as the fourth-dimensional set of laws governing evolution is a function of mind; and because of this, increases in biogenic migration and accompanying geochemical processes tend toward greater diversification and possibilities of thought and mind which have environmental-geological impact. This movement of evolution into self-reflective mind augurs the transition of the biosphere into the noosphere. The noosphere, the planetary mental envelope, is a consequence of understanding the laws of time."

12. Laws of time, or solar-galactically regulated timing frequencies, govern the biomass and its role in the evolution of the biosphere into the noosphere.

13. If biomass is constant for all geological eras, then there is a bio-homeostasis that is regulated by the timing frequencies of terrestrial evolution, and which can be mathematically formulated and applied.

14. The key to understanding the operations of the biosphere lies in determining the exact value of the biomass constant by which bio-homeostasis is maintained, yet remains capable of greater increases

in levels of biogenic diversification and rearrangement of genetic forms, which nonetheless progress toward a greater mental synthesis and environmental impact.

15. Within the biosphere, third-dimensional space regulates expansion by exerting an inescapable pressure on the two distinctive processes of life: propagation and multiplication. When maximum acceleration of propagation and multiplication of species occurs, a critical juncture is reached; the timing frequency adjusts itself, and a mutative shift occurs leading to a new evolutionary or geological era.

16. Discrete evolutionary cycles governed by timing frequencies are referred to as biomutational sequences, eras in which new forms of life emerge, evolve and impact upon each other. The biomutational sequence is purely a function of the timing frequencies.

17. According to the laws of fourth-dimensional time, the regulation of evolutionary possibilities are the functions of the linking or synchronization of two timing frequencies which create a fourth-dimensional planetary time lattice: a 260-kin cycle and a 365-kin cycle.

18. The interaction of these two cycles results in their having a 5:7 :: 7:5 relationship to each other and creates the ratio constant of the biomass within its ever-shifting biohomeostasis, in the following way:

260 : 365 = 5:7, where the spin-to-year ratio operates by the common denominator of the overtone fifth. As the galactic spin describes a time compression moved by the value of the overtone fifth, the ratio is also stated:

73 : 52 = 7:5 where 365 = 73 (x 5) and 260 = 52 (x 5).
The annual orbit may also be expressed as the lunar value of 52 (x 7) +1, where four sets of 7 (4 x = 28) are moved 13 times (28 x 13 = 364) +1 = 73 (5).

19. The two fractal relations with ratio 5:7 :: 7:5 determine the base

orbital chromatic of Earth to Sun as 73 (5) — 73 chromatics to one orbital spin. Moved by the 52 chromatics of the galactic spin, the 73 orbital chromatics create a base solar-galactic cycle of 52 annual orbits. The resulting fractal equivalent is:

73 galactic spins = 52 solar-orbital spins, or ratio 7:5.

This completes the equation of the biomass constant where the base spin to annual orbit ratio is 5:7, and the total cyclic ratio is 7:5. The common denominators of the solar-galactic timing frequencies are 73 and 52 moved by the power of the overtone fifth. The ongoing interaction of these two timing frequencies maintains the biomass constant.

20. According to the actual fourth-dimensional vigesimal mathematics, the biomass constant can be stated as 73 (73 = 3.13 = 13 to the 3rd power of 20) moved by the power of the overtone fifth. This expresses the power in time of Earth's orbital spin, where one annual cycle = 365 kin (365 = 18.5. = 5 to the 18th power of 20), moved by the overtone fifth, where 73 x 5 = 365.

21. As the moving power of the biomass constant 73, the chromatic overtone fifth is in direct resonance with the solar constant. The solar timing lattice is a function of the chromatic fifth moved by the harmonic fourth, hence the solar constant is 20 (5 x 4) expressed in fourth-dimensional vigesimal mathematics as 1.0.

22. The solar harmonic fourth is registered in the terrestrial orbit as the four solar stations: spring equinox, summer solstice, fall equinox, winter solstice, where each quarter interval is accorded the value of 18 (x 5) = 90 (x 4) = 360 or 72 (5), plus one chromatic = 365 = 73 (5), the perfect overtone fifth. Expressed in 7-day terms, 13 (x 7) = 91 x 4 = 364+1 = 73 (5).

23. The chromatic fifth overtones the power of 13 (5 +8 = 13). Thirteen is the sixth (5 +1) term in the logarithmic sequence (1, 2, 3, 5, 8, 13). Hence the solar timing lattice of the harmonic fourth and chromatic fifth overtones the sun through the power of the 13. The solar timing lattice is expressed: 1.0 (20) = 4 (5)< >(13) = 260 (= 13.0).

As the source of the galactic spin ratio, 260 represents the galactic timing lattice or 260-kin resonant frequency code.

24. 260 expressed in vigesimal mathematics is 13.0, the 13th power of 20. Moved by the overtone fifth the galactic spin ratio is 52:5; moved by the harmonic fourth, the ratio is 65:4.

25. The 260-kin galactic frequency code governs solar and terrestrial evolution. Expressed as 65 harmonics, the 13.0 code is expressed 13 (5) x 4, where 13 (5) = 8 (8) +1. This formulation governs the timing lattice through which the terrestrial DNA organizes itself as biomass in accord with cosmic measure. 8 (8) = 64 is the frequency number governing the set of codons by which the biomass constant plays out its biomutational sequences. The 65th harmonic, which in the radial formulation is the 33rd or central term, is the +1 factor which allows evolutionary sequences the power of biomutation.

26. The solar timing lattice constant 1.0 (13) {13.0} is maintained at the Earth's core and held in balance by the terrestrial satellite, the moon. The Earth core constant is a function of 20 {1.0} moved by the power of 13, hence the core ratio 20:13. This ratio functions as extra-low frequency pulsations which establish the Earth's timing lattice. 20:13 is the solar-terrestrial transduction of galactic-solar 13:20.

27. Solar and terrestrial core, and biomass constants are expressions of the value of 5 and 13. The biomass constant governing the sum expression of the living corpus is 73/5, where 73 is the value 3.13; the frequency ratio governing the inert geochemical content of the Earth and biosphere is 20/13. Hence we have biomass ratio 73/5(3.13)(5) = 18.5, or 365 kin, and solar-terrestrial ratio 20/13, 1.0(13) = 13.0 or 260 kin.

28. The relation of the 260 kin to the 365 kin can also be expressed as 260 +105 = 365 +/-105, where the value of the differential 105 in vigesimal notation is expressed as 5.5 or the overtone fifth to the fifth power of 20. The differential of 5.5 expresses the power of

linked chromatics which unifies the 260(13.0) and the 365(18.5) orders of kin.

29. Linked chromatics describes the direct and unmediated relationship in time between solar-galactic radiations (electromagnetic), terrestrial-lunar magnetism (gravitational) and DNA-governed biomass (biopsychic). These triple-linked chromatic relations assume the fourth-dimensional ordering power of radialization in which all elements are immediately bound to all others.

30. Through fourth-dimensional timing frequencies the human component of the DNA biomass is in direct relation to the solar-galactic order. The human is a mobile root function of the 64+1 (= 5 x 13) DNA code. This code expresses itself in the human type as four mobile appendages moved by the power of five (digits) creating a 20-digit mobile entity. The 20-digital form recapitulates the fractal solar power of 20 (1.0).

The trunk, or root, form of the human recapitulates the chromatic overtone power of 5 through the distribution of the 5 biopsychic power centers of the human form: crown, throat, heart, solar plexus, and root. Moved by the power of 13 kin, the 20-digital form yields the galactic timing frequency of 260. The five biopsychic centers moved by the power of 13 = 65, the DNA code 64 + 1, the same as the number of harmonics constituting the galactic frequency code of 260 kin.

This demonstrates that the intrinsic powers of solar-galactic biomutation are held completely within the human form. The more direct is the index of communication of the human with itself and with the terrestrial-lunar and solar-galactic orders, the more immediate is the power of the human to regulate itself.

31. The mobile root of the human, both individually and collectively, like the rest of the biomass, is regulated by the biomass constant 73 (5). The galactic spin(13.0), multiplied by the biomass constant (3.13) equals the biomass constant 73 (5) (18.5) multiplied by the galactic constant 52 (2.12), or 52 annual orbits, 73 spins, 3,796 (9.9.16) chromatics, or 18,890 kin (2.7.9.0). In other words, one human solar-galactic cycle = 52 annual orbits of the Earth = 73 galac-

tic spins = 3,796 chromatics = 18,980 kin.

32. Regulation of the biomass by the constant 73 (5) is maintained by two fourth-dimensional timing orders which find kin equivalence in one rotation of the Earth on its axis. The rotation of the Earth on its axis assures that at all times one half of the Earth is receiving solar radiation while the other is bathed in galactic radiation. From this fact comes the division of the axial spin into a day count and a night count. The day count of the spin is base 20 (1.0). Moved by the power of 13, the day count consists of a sequence of 20 kin repeated 13 times. Each of these 13 sequences is a harmonic run of five time cells.

The night count of the spin is base 13 (13). Moved by the power of 20, the night count consists of a sequence of 13 kin repeated 20 times. Each of these 20 sequences is a wavespell of 13 kin. Annually there are 18.5 harmonic runs and 28 wavespells of 13 kin. (28 x 13) +1 = 365 = 73 fifths =18. 5 harmonic runs. The sum of 365 day kin and 365 night kin = 730, or 73 (x 10), hence the chromatic constant appears again. The day-count night-count ratio can also be expressed $1/_2$ 730 = 36.5, fractal of the number of days (365) in an annual terrestrial orbit. The quarter days of the annual orbit accumulate at the rate of 13 per 52 years, 52 being the galactic constant.

33. There are 73 (3.13) orbital chromatics to 65 (3.5) galactic harmonics. The frequency difference between the two sums is 8, the frequency code number for a galactic octave, which moved by its own power yields 64 ((8 x 8)+1 = 65), the power of the DNA code governing the biomass. The difference between the 52 fifths of the 260-kin code and the 65 (64+1) harmonics of the power of the DNA code is 13, the cosmic frequency power. The difference between 52 and 73 is 21, the seventh term in the logarithmic sequence (1, 2, 3, 5, 8, 13, 21), where 21 = 13+8, 13 being the difference between 52 and 65, and 8 the difference between 65 and 73. In this descending ratio, the next term is 5, which added to 73 = 78, or 13 x 6. 52 is the galactic constant, 64 the biogenetic constant, and 73 the orbital constant regulating the biomass.

34. The galactic constant 52(5) = 260 x 73, the orbital biomass

constant = 52 solar years. The 52-year cycle is the minimum base galactic unit for identifying the human biomass within the solar-galactic order. The galactic 52-year constant also yields the formula for regulation of the biomutational sequence. That is, 52 to the order of 100 (x 5.0, or 20 to the 5th power) = 5,200 years. As the fractal power of 52(5.0), 5,200 years is one fifth of a total biomutational sequence of 26,000 years (5,200 x 5). In other words the minimum biomutational sequence is 26,000 years. 26,000 years represents the evolutionary sequence of homo sapiens, the ultimate form of biomass whose powers of complex mentation have acutely affected the biosphere, causing it to come to its next pressure point of maximum multiplication and propagation.

35. Plotted as a radial wave, the curve of biomass acceleration is barely perceptible, i.e. virtually constant, during the first four-fifths of the biomutational sequence. At the beginning of the last 5,200-year fractal sequence, the rate of biogenic migration of atoms became mentally and technologically excited by innovations in agriculture, hydraulic engineering and metallurgy. Following the fractal formulation of the timing frequencies, this process of unprecedented mentation and biogenic migration reached its point of irreversible technological acceleration 260 years prior to the conclusion of the 26,000 year biomutational sequence. By fractal wave condensation, the triggering to the next biomutational sequence begins 26 years prior to the conclusion of the 26,000 year sequence. Because this most minimum sequence represents the final advancement of the process of mentation into the biopsheric equation, the biohomeostasis of the biomass has reached a point of dynamic disequilibrium.

36. Since the pressure of all of the evolutionary points of the biomass exerted upon themselves, aided by mentation and technology, is now at a point of bursting, the biomass constant itself is endangered. If the biomass constant were to be disequilibrated out of its 73-orbital chromatic flow, the result would be the complete disequilibration and breaking up of the planetary sphere, sooner than later.

37. Dynamic equilibrium can only be restored through acceptance and understanding of the fourth-dimensional timing frequencies. The very act of accepting, understanding and applying the 13:20 timing frequency will establish the basis for a new biohomeostasis, and the transition to the noosphere. As soon as this is accomplished, a new level of biomass equality is automatically attained, and the next biomutational sequence can begin. Since the next biomutational sequence is completed as the noosphere, an entirely new order of being is to be defined: the bioholomass, the integration of third- and fourth-dimensional orders of being. The mental synthesis of the bioholomass synchronized with itself in time creates the conditions for universal transcension: the entry of the whole system Earth into the supermind of galactic being.

In sum:

1) The biomass constant is a function of the orbital chromatic constant 73(5); the orbital chromatic constant regulates biomutational and geological sequences of planet Earth in accord with solar-galactic timing frequencies. When multiplication and propagation of biomass reach maximum pressure points, a frequency adjustment of the timing frequency occurs. This adjustment is a normalization which returns dissonant frequencies due to pressure to a new state of equal conditions in accord with the base 20:13 frequency. The equation for the biomass constant is:

13 (28) + 1: 28 (13)+1 :: 52 (7) +1: 91 (4) +1 = 73 (5), where the first two equivalences are: moons (13) to wavespells (28), and the second two: weeks (52) to harmonics (91).

Within the 13 moons, the sequence of 73 chromatics is established in five overtone patterns, where:

Moons	1, 6, 11	chromatically fractal each other
Moons	2, 7, 12	chromatically fractal each other
Moons	3, 8, 13	chromatically fractal each other
Moons	4. 9	chromatically fractal each other
Moons	5, 10	chromatically fractal each other

2) The level of progressive mentation and technological complexification leads the biosphere to a hyper-biomutational adjustment called the transition to the noosphere. The noosphere is brought about by the human component of the biomass understanding time as the fourth dimension, which, by making conscious the unconscious timing frequencies, initiates a new level of conscious planetary self-regulation.

3) The fractal timetable of the final biospheric-noospheric transition:

1. -26 years (AD 1987) mental technological complexification peaks; entry into condition of dynamic disequilibrium.
2. -21 years (AD 1992) time shift commences, disequilibrium peaks.
3. -20 years (AD 1993) biosphere-noosphere transition commences, time becomes conscious in humans.
Initiates 260th katun of Mayan Great Cycle.
4. -13 years (AD 2000) biomass reconstituted as bioholomass, integration of third- and fourth-dimensional levels of being.
5. -0 = AD 2013, point of universal transcension, mental synthesis of bioholomass through solar-galactic synchronization; entry into realm of galactic supermind.

Kin 185: Red Electric Serpent
Establishes the Red Galactic Spectrum
Rhythmic Moon 7
Blue Cosmic Storm Year.
Fulfillment of the Call of Pacal Votan
José A. Argüelles, PhD
Independent Hawai'ian Kingdom
Archipelago of Hawai'i

OTHER INFORMATION

The 13 Spectral Chromatics

There are 13 spectral chromatics, five kin per chromatic, creating one 65-kin galactic season. The four galactic seasons are Red Serpent, White Dog, Blue Eagle, Yellow Sun (4 x 13 = 52 spectral chromatics). The power of 13 circulates the four primal color powers 52 times to create the 52 varieties of spectral chromatics. The same principle governs the circulation of the solar years to create the 52-year solar-galactic cycle.

Each of the 13 spectral chromatics is coded by one of the four colors to create the full spectrum of the 52 spectral chromatics.

1) 3-7: electric-resonant
   spectral chromatic   red   white   blue   yellow
2) 8-12: galactic-crystal
   spectral chromatic   white   blue   yellow   red
3) 13-4: cosmic self-existing
   spectral chromatic   blue   yellow   red   white
4) 5-9: overtone-solar
   spectral chromatic   yellow   red   white   blue
5) 10-1: planetary-magnetic
   spectral chromatic   red   white   blue   yellow
6) 2-6: lunar-rhythmic
   spectral chromatic   white   blue   yellow   red
7) 7-11: resonant-spectral
   spectral chromatic   blue   yellow   red   white
8) 12-3: crystal electric
   spectral chromatic   yellow   red   white   blue
9) 4-8: self-existing-galactic
   spectral chromatic   red   white   blue   yellow
10) 9-13: solar-cosmic
    spectral chromatic   white   blue   yellow   red
11) 1-5: magnetic-overtone
    spectral chromatic   blue   yellow   red   white
12) 6-10: rhythmic-planetary
    spectral chromatic   yellow   red   white   blue
13) 11-2: spectral-lunar
    spectral chromatic   red   white   blue   yellow

Note: each season is read vertically down so that the first chromatic and the last chromatic correspond in color.

The Red serpent season begins on the third kin of the blue night wavespell 15.
The White Dog season begins on the third kin of the yellow star wavespell 20.
The Blue Eagle season begins on the third kin of the red skywalker wavespell 5.
The Yellow Sun season begins on the third kin of the white mirror wavespell 10.

Note: all wavespells are signal family whose wavespell numbers correspond to the codespell numbers of the polar kin, i.e. serpent 5, dog 10, eagle 15, sun 20.

The four five-kin spectral chromatics are:

    1) red serpent-moon blood chromatic (right foot)
    2) white dog-wizard truth chromatic (left hand)
    3) blue eagle-storm sky chromatic (left foot)
    4) yellow sun-seed fire chromatic (right hand)

The 73 Overtone Chromatics

There are 73 (72+1) overtone chromatics which code and govern the biomass constant. Each of these 73 overtone chromatics runs from a gateway to a signal family seal. The four types of overtone chromatics are:

    1) red moon-skywalker overtone chromatic
    2) white wizard-mirror overtone chromatic
    3) blue storm-night overtone chromatic
    4) yellow seed-star overtone chromatic

Each of the four gateway seals codes each of the four years, which combined with the 13 tones creates the 52-year solar galactic cycle. The signal family seal of the chromatic that codes the year is always the seal of the day out of time, which also bears the same galactic tone as codes the year, e.g. if the year is magnetic seed, the day out of time is magnetic star; if the year is lunar moon, the day out of time is lunar skywalker, etc.

The overtone pulsar code governs the appearance of the overtone chromatics within the 13 moons. This means that the overtone chromatics code the days of the magnetic, rhythmic and spectral moons in the same sequence. The same is true then for the lunar, resonant and crystal moons; the electric, galactic and cosmic moons; the self-existing and solar moons; and the overtone and planetary moons.

Overtone Chromatic			Days of the Moon	Moons
1*	29*	57*	1-5	Magnetic, Rhythmic, Spectral
2	30	58	6-10	Magnetic, Rhythmic, Spectral
3	31	59	11-15	Magnetic, Rhythmic, Spectral
4	32	60	16-20	Magnetic, Rhythmic, Spectral
5*	33*	61*	21-25	Magnetic, Rhythmic, Spectral
6	34	62	26-2	Magnetic, Rhythmic, Spectral
7	35	63	3-7	Lunar, Resonant, Crystal
8	36	64	8-12	Lunar, Resonant, Crystal
9	37	65	13-17	Lunar, Resonant, Crystal
10	38	66	18-22	Lunar, Resonant, Crystal
11	39	67	23-27	Lunar, Resonant, Crystal
12	40	68	28-4	Lunar, Resonant, Crystal
13*	41*	69*	5-9	Electric, Galactic, Cosmic
14	42	70	10-14	Electric, Galactic, Cosmic
15	43	71	15-19	Electric, Galactic, Cosmic
16	44	72	20-24	Electric, Galactic, Cosmic
17*	45*	73*	25-1	Electric, Galactic, Cosmic + Day Out of Time
18	46		2-6	Self-Existing Solar
19	47		7-11	Self-Existing Solar
20	48		12-16	Self-Existing Solar
21*	49*		17-21	Self-Existing Solar
22	50		22-26	Self-Existing Solar
23	51		27-3	Self-Existing Solar
24	52		4-8	Overtone Planetary
25*	53*		9-13	Overtone Planetary
26	54		14-18	Overtone Planetary
27	55		19-23	Overtone Planetary
28	56		24-28	Overtone Planetary

*The first day of each of these 19 overtone chromatics codes the 19 Galactic Portals of the Galactic Compass. This means that each of these 19 overtone chromatics begins with the seal that governs the year, i.e. for a yellow seed year, these 19 overtone chromatics will each begin with the yellow seed seal; for a red moon year, they will each begin with the red moon seal, etc.

The 19 galactic portal days which begin these 19 overtone chromatics correspond to the initial dates of the 18 Vinals + one five-day Uayeb (overtone chromatic 73) of the Haab, the traditional Mayan Solar Calendar. Each Vinal is 20 days (18 X 20 = 360); with the five-day Uayeb, this creates the 365-day solar year cycle.

The 18 Vinals of the Haab solar frequency cycle
The 19 correlate dates and the 73 overtone chromatics

Vinal	13 Moon	Gregorian	Overtone Chromatics
1. 0 Pop	=01.01	=07.26	1-4
The one who knows			
2. 0 Uo	=01.21	=08.15	5-8
Listens in silence			
3. 0 Zip	=02.13	=09.04	9-12
In order to integrate the universe			
4. 0 Zotz	=03.05	=09.24	13-16
Based on knowledge			
5. 0 Tzec	=03.25	=10.14	17-20
That reaches the foundations			
6. 0 Xul	=04.17	=11.03	21-24
Where with great wisdom a seed is sown			
7. 0 Yaxkin	=05.09	=11.23	25-28
= 140 days, five perfect moons			
A little ray of the hidden sun			
8. 0 Mol	=06.01	=12.13	29-32
Which unifies all of the pieces			
9. 0 Ch'en	=06.21	=01.02	33-36
To enter into the well of the inner wisdom			
10. 0 Yax	=07.13	=01.22	37-40
Where the student clears the mind, taking account of what is not yet ripe			

11. 0 Sac   =08.05   =02.11   41-44
Dissipating the clouds of doubt, raising her/himself up
12. 0 Ceh   =08.25   =03.03   45-48
Breaks with habitual caution, and reaches the white light
13. 0 Mac   =09.17   =03.23   49-52
    = 260 days, one galactic spin
Closing the equivocating part and entering a trance
14. 0 Kankin   =10.09 (=1.01)   =04.12 (=07.26) 53-56
    = 280 days, ten perfect moons
Receives the light of one who knows
15. 0 Moan   =11.01   =05.02   57-60
In order to see into the darkness
16. 0 Pax   =11.21   =05.22   61-64
Touching a music of the future
17. 0 Kayab   =12.13   =06.11   65-68
With the song and the rhythm
18. 0 Cumhu   =13.05   =07.01   69-72
Located in the correct place where the food of divination is obtained
19. 0 Uayeb   =13.25   =07.21   73
                    3 Uayeb = 13.28 = 07.24
                    4 Uayeb = 07.25 = Day out of time
All that is lacking in order to obtain the precious stone

(The 'precious stone' is the *tun* which is the 360-day cycle; the five-day Uayeb or 73rd chromatic is the wisdom that completes the annual solar cycle.)

These 19 correlate dates of the Vinal cycle correspond to the outermost green ring of the Dreamspell Galactic Compass. The 73 chromatics are the number of the biomass constant, conscious regulation of which transits the biosphere into the noosphere. The names of the Vinal-solar frequency cycle are from the original Mayan, and the text for each recounts the sequence of the cycle of solar wisdom.

JOSÉ ARGÜELLES

José Argüelles (born 1939), planetary whole systems anthropologist, received his Ph.D. in Art History and Aesthetics from the University of Chicago in 1969. In a distinguished career as an educator, he taught at Princeton University, University of California, Evergreen State College, San Francisco State University, San Francisco Institute of Art, the Naropa Institute, the University of Colorado, and the Union Graduate School.

His pioneering books resulting from investigations into human whole systems include: *Mandala* (1972), *A Psychophysical Aesthetic* (1972), *The Transformative Vision: Reflections on the Nature and History of Human Expression* (1975, 1992), *Surfers of the Zuvuya* (1989), *The Arcturus Probe* (1992) and most importantly *Earth Ascending: An Illustrated Treatise on the Law Governing Whole Systems* (1984, 1988).

As one of the founders of Earth Day (First Whole Earth Festival, Davis, California, 1970), Argüelles is a career activist for peace and the planetary transformation of consciousness. He and his wife and partner, Lloydine, founded the Planet Art Network (1983), promoting the revival of the Nicholas Roerich Peace Pact and Banner of Peace (1935). Combining investigations of the Roerich Peace Pact with his lifetime study of the mathematics and prophecies of the Mayan calendar, Argüelles initiated the Harmonic Convergence, August 16-17 1987, global meditation and planetary peace event.

Following his unraveling of the Mayan calendar code in his international bestseller, *The Mayan Factor: Path Beyond Technology* (1987), Argüelles, with his wife, continued his scientific and mathematical investigations of the timing frequency underlying the Mayan calendar system of ancient Central America. The result of their research was the discovery of the 12:60—13:20 timing frequencies and the breakthrough set of tools and proofs of the mathematics of the fourth-dimensional time, *Dreamspell: The Journey of Timeship Earth 2013* (1991, 1992), the *13-Moon Calendar* (1992), *A Treatise on Time Viewed from Its Own Dimension* (1992), now published as *The Call of Pacal Votan: Time is the Fourth Dimension*, and finally *Telektonon: the Talking Stone of Prophecy*, the 13-moon calendar, prophecy, game and universal peace plan (1993-94). José Argüelles is also co-author of *Galactic Human Handbook/Entering the New Time*.

VICTORYNET

The Planetary Rainbow Tribe Networking Guide

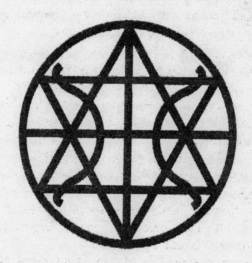

OPERATION VICTORY

*is dedicated to coordinating the advancement of the Oneness of
Humanity and Planetary Transformation*

The majority of profits from the sale of the resources listed in this section are used to support ongoing educational work in the form of books, videos, VictoryNet and all the other tools which inspire an experience of time as the fourth dimension.

THE GALACTIC CULTURAL STRATEGY

A curriculum instituted by Planetary Calendar Council groups to activate the Rainbow Tribe. Time is the basis of culture; below are the tools for understanding Galactic Time.

1) Dreamspell Calendar of Planetary Service, 13-Moon 28-Day
PM 5   Black and white wall calendar $10.00*
PM 5a   Full color pocket calendar $13.00*
This takes us to the first stage of galactic knowledge where we learn the difference between the false Gregorian 12:60 time and the true galactic 13:20 time, reconnecting us to our natural rhythms.

2) Telektonon, Game of Prophecy
PM 10 ....$39.00*
As we increase the numbers of humanity who follow the 13-Moon Calendar, we increase the general bio-telepathic field of resonance. This Telektonon playing board is the sword of light, the technology of telepathy.

3) Telektonon, Teaching Video
VT 12 ....$29.95*
A comprehensive introductory video to help you with the game.

4) Dreamspell, The Journey of Timeship Earth 2013 Kit
PM 9 ....$39.00*
While the 13-Moon Calendar and the Telektonon fulfill the purpose of biologically and telepathically restoring the human to its rightful role and place within the planetary biosphere, it is the Dreamspell which provides the social reorganizing factor of the new time, the operating tools for navigating fourth-dimensional time.

5) Dreamspell, Teaching Video, by José & Lloydine Argüelles
VT 11 ....$29.95*
A comprehensive introductory video to help you with the kit.

6) Galactic Human Handbook / Entering the New Time and Creating Planetary Groups, book by Sheldon Nidle & José Argüelles
PM3A..$11.95*
Galactic civilization, the new timing frequency and the forming of Planetary Advocate Groups, Planetary Calendar Councils, the Planet Art Network to help the transformation of the planet and human society.

7) The Call of Pacal Votan: Time is the Fourth Dimension, book by José Argüelles
PM 11 . . . .$11.95*
A complete description of the discovery of the 12:60—13:20 timing frequencies and of the mathematical laws governing the radial matrix of fourth-dimensional time.

8) Dreamspell, Calendar Software
IBM   PM7 . . . .$13.00
Macintosh   PM8 . . . .$13.00
With this software you find your galactic signature and place in the Rainbow Tribe. You will also find the meditation of the day.

9) The Mayan Factor, The Path Beyond Technology by José Argüelles
PM 12 . . . .$12.95

10) Surfers of the Zuvuya: Tales of Interdimensional Travel by José Argüelles
PM13 . . . .$15.00

  * Wholesale: 40% discount for 12 items or more, plus shipping.

OTHER INFORMATION

'Galactic Time' Workshop — by Sheldon Nidle
Based on the Mayan calendar and José Argüelles's Dreamspell Game. Understanding Galactic Time will be useful in the new galactic civilization that is emerging.
● 20 Sacred Glyphs ● 13 Tones of Creation ● Wavespells and Castles ● Tzolkin ● Haab   VT5 for a 4-hour video & 18-page booklet @ $50

'Becoming a Galactic Human' Workshop — by Sheldon Nidle
This workshop presents what it means to become a galactic human along with an in-depth look at Fluid Management leadership principles and the Ral-Ba meditation technique.
● What it means to be a galactic human ● Theory and practice of fluid management ● Exploring group consciousness ● Fluid management exercises ● Ral-Ba: a new meditation to anchor the higher frequencies ● A method to empower and rejuvenate the mind ● Nature of the new realignments of the chakras ● How to better adjust your light body to the new chakras   VT7 for a 4-hour video @ $50.00

The Day Out of Time video — José and Lloydine Argüelles
Watching this video allows you to participate in one of the most powerful ceremonies at the end of this 26,000-year Mayan Cycle. Sunrise, midday and sunset ceremonies of a planetary rainbow gathering at Serpent Mount, Ohio, on July 25, 1995, A Day Out of Time. Interviews with José and Lloydine Argüelles on the Mayan Calendar.

VT13 for a 104-minute video @ $29.95

Also available: **You Are Becoming a Galactic Human** — book by
Sheldon Nidle & Virginia Essene $11.95

To keep in touch with the latest news and developments, including regular updates from José Argüelles, see VictoryNet Website at
http://www.victory-net.com/
It is also possible to join the VictoryNet Round Table — see page 139

Ordering

US orders: See Order Form. Send order to:

> **Operation Victory USA**
> 1450 4th Street, Suite 6
> Berkeley, CA 94710
> USA
> Tel +1 (510) 559-8102, Fax +1 (510) 559-9493

For audio and video tapes, add 8.25% California tax plus shipping and handling charges. For printed materials add shipping and handling charges. Foreign orders multiply shipping by 3 (or order from regional centers). See over for US and Canada shipping charges.

Wholesale: 40% discount for 12 items or more, plus shipping

Outside USA: to find out regional prices and shipping and handling charges, contact your regional center:

Operation Victory Europe	**Operation Victory New Zealand**
Parkmount House	PO Box 66-067
10 St Leonards Road	Beach Haven
Forres IV36 0DW, Scotland	Auckland 1310
Tel/Fax +44 01309 673312	New Zealand
	Tel/Fax +64 9 483 5174

Operation Victory Australia
40 George Street
North Hobart, Tasmania 7000
Australia
Tel +61 02 346687, Fax +61 02 312578

US AND CANADA SHIPPING AND HANDLING CHARGES		
Subtotal	US	Canada
Up to $20.00	Add $4.00	Add $5.00
$20.01-$40.00	$5.00	$6.00
$40.01-$60.00	$6.00	$7.00
$60.01-$80.00	$8.00	$10.00

In US and Canada, shipping is UPS ground or equivalent.
For rush shipping call (510) 559-8102 or Fax (510) 559 9493

OPERATION VICTORY
GENERAL ORDER FORM
(To be detached or photocopied)

Name _____

Address _____

_____ City _____

State/Country _____ Zip/Post Code _____

Phone (optional) _____

QUANTITY	PRICE	DESCRIPTION	AMOUNT
_____	_____	_____	_____
_____	_____	_____	_____
_____	_____	_____	_____
_____	_____	_____	_____
_____	_____	_____	_____
_____	_____	_____	_____
_____	_____	_____	_____
_____	_____	_____	_____
_____	_____	_____	_____

Please check if first order ☐

Date _____   Total _____

* Shipping and handling _____

(For California residents) 8.25% Sales Tax _____

Grand Total _____

☐ Cash   ☐ Money Order   ☐ Check

☐ Mastercard/Visa no:

_____

Expiry date _____ Signature _____

Thank you for your order
Send with payment to your regional distribution point

VICTORYNET ROUND TABLE

- Round Table will connect you worldwide with lightworkers and planetary groups
- Round Table will supply the most current information from around the globe
- Round Table will keep you up to date about spiritual events
- Round Table will synchronize and coordinate our efforts to shift the mass consciousness

Get online with a local Internet provider and once you have your e-mail address, fill out the signup procedure below.

VICTORYNET ROUND TABLE SIGNUP PROCEDURE
(To be detached or photocopied)

Step 1: Complete the following:

Name _____

Address _____

City _____

State/Country _____ Zip/post code _____

User Name _____

Password (5 or more characters) _____

Step 2: Enclose the following:
US$84.00 yearly subscription

☐ Visa/Master Card   ☐ My check is enclosed

Visa/Master Card no. _____

Expiry date _____

Planetary Group Information
If you are a member of a Planetary Group, please complete the following information. As soon as your group has formed, please forward the following information to us and advise us of any changes. All groups and their locations will be posted in the guide.

Group name _____

Group function _____

continued over . . . .

E-mail _____

Liaison name _____

Phone _____

Address _____

City _____

State/Country _____ Zip/post code _____

Mail to: Operation Victory, 1450 4th Street, Suite 6, Berkeley, CA 94710, USA. Tel +1 (510) 559 8102, Fax +1 (510) 559 9493.

http://www.victory-net.com/

WEBSITES ON VICTORYNET

VictoryNet is the first planetary computer network dedicated to the advancement of the oneness of humanity and planetary transformation. VictoryNet is the place in space and time to tune in to the virtual community of consciousness (seminars, workshops, books, newsletters, products, etc) and all that is occurring on the planet to bring in the light.

We invite you to become part of the victory, the net and celebration of humanity. Listed below are the packages and rates to choose from for your own website within the VictoryNet, a living mandala.

Primary Resource Site Package

- An individual listing in the VictoryNet Resource Site Index, which appears by category on the VictoryNet home page. Your pages appear within VictoryNet. The guide header will appear on top of your pages. Your URL address will be:

    http://www.victory-net.com/your name

- Up to four pages of text and images, designed for easy readability. The first page gives you space to present your logo, an introductory paragraph, and two pages for your basic presentation, with up to 250 words on each page. The last page is for a bio or story about you, or the people who are part of your organization.

Two photos or images. We suggest you use one on your first page and the other on your bio page. This is VictoryNet's standard format. Yours may vary according to your needs.

Introductory Level Resource Page

This listing package includes one page with one graphic or logo, an introductory paragraph and up to 150 words of text.

How Can You List in VictoryNet?

It's easy. Just mail the application form with your payment for the composition charge, the posting charge (if applicable) and any extra charges.

Listing Rates

Take advantage of our special introductory offer which waives the entire first year's maintenance charges for both our four and one page resource packages.

Composition Charges
Primary four page package $485
Introductory one page package $175

Site Maintenance (Posting) Fees
Primary four page package $245/year
Introductory one page package $145/year
Additional pages $25/year

Additional Services
Extra images $20/scan, plus $20 setup
Text changes $40/hour, with $25 minimum
Hand-keys copy $40/hour
Copywriting and editing $50/hour
Graphic design $50/hour
Links to other sites $10 within VictoryNet
                              $20 outside VictoryNet

Downloadable audio, video or text files:
$25 minimum for setup, plus $25/megabyte per year with a 1 megabyte minimum.

Call for information on our rates for video filming, digitizing and editing; speciality programming and hit list reports.

What You Need to Send Us . . .
Include your text and images on disk as described below:
• Send your text on a Windows, IBM or Macintosh formatted 3.5" diskette. Save your wordprocessed text in Text Format if possible (include line breaks). Please indicate which section of text belongs on each page. Also send a printed copy of your text.
• Photographs, logos, or other images digitized and saved to diskette.
• Images and photos for VictoryNet to scan should be good quality. Please send only professional quality graphics.

Any client-composed pages must be professionally done to our specifications. Please contact us for specifications and setup.

VICTORYNET WEBSITE APPLICATION FORM

(To be detached or photocopied)

CATEGORY

☐ Primary site package   ☐ Intro level page

☐ Text/images enclosed on disk & paper

☐ Text/graphics on paper only

Posting fee _____

Composition charge _____

Editing/other fees _____

Subtotal _____

Total _____

CREDIT CARD

☐ VISA   ☐ MasterCard

Account number _____

Expiry date _____

Charge authorization signature _____

Organization & contact person _____

_____

E-mail _____

Phone _____

Best time to call _____

Address _____

_____

City _____

State/Country _____ Zip/Post Code _____

Please make check payable to Operation Victory, 1450 4th Street, Suite 6, Berkeley, CA 94170, USA.
Tel +1 (510) 559 8102, Fax +1 (510) 559 9493